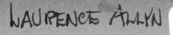

PELICAN

FISHLORE

BRITISH FRESHWATER FISHES

BY

A. F. MAGRI MacMAHON

(A161)

PELICAN BOOKS

FISHLORE

BRITISH FRESHWATER FISHES

BY

A. F. Magri MacMahon

PUBLISHED BY

PENGUIN BOOKS

HARMONDSWORTH MIDDLESEX ENGLAND

245 FIFTH AVENUE NEW YORK U.S.A.

First published 1946

MADE AND PRINTED IN GREAT BRITAIN FOR PENGUIN BOOKS LTD.
BY HAZELL, WATSON AND VINEY, LTD., LONDON AND AYLESBURY

TO ALL MY FRIENDS

ANIMAL, VEGETABLE, MINERAL—AND HUMAN

GRATEFULLY

Any resemblance of the characters in
the book to living or dead persons is
purely natural, and nobody
regrets it more than the author.

CONTENTS

Plates are reproduced by permission of the Zoological Society of London (Plate 1), Dr. Douglas P. Wilson (Plate 2), and W. B. and S. C. Johnston, D.Sc. (Plates 3 to 16), to all of whom I tender my thanks.

GENERAL SECTION

You, *Brother General Reader*, know little of fishes, just as I know little of your job or hobby. You know little, and care less—until they are nicely fried. Fishes are slimy, goggly, cold "things," smelling unpleasantly on the fishmonger's slab. They are proverbially "dumb" in both the English and the American senses: "Why, only those cracked fellows of anglers would take an interest in them." Are you so sure, Brother? Do you know that fishes form the largest group of vertebrate animals in existence? If you are impressed by figures, what do you think of these? There are at least 25,000 different species (or thousands more, according to some naturalists), showing an almost nightmarish variety of shapes, sizes, habits and surroundings. Some are so beautiful as to attract submarine artists, who delight to paint them in their native haunts. Others, as you will discover, are quaint and fascinating in their oddity. Come, Brother, for a few pence I offer you the keys of a new kingdom. Don't be afraid of big, bad scientific words, I have left them out. And, be it whispered, I have included some hints on the cooking of fish. Your wife (or, even more, her husband) will find them interesting.

Big Brother Ichthyologist, this book is not for you. There is nothing in it that you don't know and much that might earn your disapproval. The omissions are many and at times glaring. I have, for instance, written at length about Cyprinids, with hardly a mention of "pharyngeals." Your reading would only single out (and point out, I hope) many mistakes, and I should be the only gainer. No, big Brother, this book is *not* for you.

Brother Angler, I hope you will find this volume useful. We know, you and I, that many fishes are difficult to recognize. You could give me dozens of instances when a fellow angler mistook (fancy that!) a Bleak for a Dace or a Carp for a Tench. You would never make a mistake like that, I'm sure, but you are, maybe, a wee bit at sea on the subject of hybrids—and small wonder. Well, that is where this book comes in. It may help to throw light on that and similar problems.

I have included a very few angling hints. These, of course, are not meant for you; you know much more already. I am not trying to compete with expert treatises on this subject. Tight lines, Brother!

For you, *Brother and Sister Highbrow*, the only interesting study is human "psychology," especially if that human is yourself. The one subject worthy of your attention is Man—which, I'm told, embraces Woman. Still, the early embryo of the Dogfish is uncomfortably like the early human embryo. The fierce voracity of the Pike, the craftiness of the Carp and the blithe *joie de vivre* of the Bleak have their counterparts in the world of men. Why, you may find that some of your friends display distinctly fishy characteristics, and that a study of fishes may help you to a charitable understanding of men (or women).

Dear young *Brother Boy* (and you, young *Sister Tomboy*), it was chiefly of you that I thought when I wrote this book. Long, long ago, when I, too, was young, I wanted to know *all* about *every* plant and creature that I saw, just as to-day you want to. I had many grown-ups to tell me, but I soon found out that they didn't know much. With books I had no better fortune. Those I could buy or understand were of little use, for they all described the same things and them only—the things everybody knew. The books that could have helped me were so big, so expensive, so grown-up, and so dull that I could not cope with them. So I decided that I would write myself the book I wanted, and I started off with Birds and Fishes, confident that it would be a quick and easy task. Forty years later, having studied a lot and learned very little, and still struggling with my profound ignorance, I have managed to finish this section of the book I planned when I was your age. I hope you will enjoy it and find it useful. I hope even more that it may spur you to want to learn more, much more, because few things will bring you so much contentment, comfort and happy work as the pursuit of Knowledge and Truth.

I

FISH AND THEIR HISTORY

> "O scaly, slippery, wet, swift, staring wights,
> What is't ye do? What life lead?"
>
> *Leigh Hunt.*

"Fish" is a word used very often and very loosely to describe any kind of creature living in the water. By the addition of a prefix or an adjective, it is applied to coelenterates (jellyfish), crustaceans and molluscs (shellfish), and even to humans, as I have reason to know.

It will be necessary, therefore, to make clear that in this book we shall apply the term "fish" only to those aquatic animals which have a backbone (vertebrates), a brain and spinal cord, breathe throughout their lives by means of gills, and have fins to assist them in movement. We shall therefore include in this little work even the Lampreys (Cyclostomata) and the Sharks and Rays (Selachians), which are widely separated from the Bony Fishes by many important peculiarities.

If a long genealogy is a good claim to superiority, fishes ought to be the highest class of the vertebrates. Their history begins long before that of any other group of backboned animals, about 330 million years ago. The first traces of fishes are found in the form of tiny conical teeth in the Lower Silurian beds of Russia, and in skin plates of the same period unearthed in the United States. Better fossils are found in the Upper Silurian deposits of the Ludlow "Bone-bed," full of fish bones and spines. During the Devonian System fishes developed considerably, and their fossils are abundant. These primitive fishes belonged to the Shark, Sturgeon and Lungfish groups and to an extinct type with the body protected by large plates forming a rigid armour. Their remains are found in the Old Red Sandstone of Wales, Northern Scotland and of the Orkneys. The development and evolution of fishes continued in Carboniferous and Permian times, when more

and more fishes left the shallow waters near the shore and took
to the deep sea. The skeleton, formerly of gristle, began to
become more bony and the skin armour to diminish. In the
Rhaetic beds near Penarth many fish bones are found, together
with the teeth of a Lung-fish very similar to a species living to-day
in Australia. In Jurassic days, when Portland stone was being
deposited, some fishes appeared that form a connecting-link with
the true Bony Fishes or Teleostei. In Cretaceous times, when the
Chalk hills of the Downs were being slowly formed in clear sea
water, these Bony Fishes prospered and increased in numbers,
taking the place of the Ganoids (Sturgeon group); many of them
had slender fin rays and a rather light skeleton, suggesting deep
waters.

Some 70 million years ago, by the time the clay on which
London rests was settling on the bottom of a shallow sea, Sharks,
Rays and Bony Fishes were dominant, and their remains are
fairly frequent; with luck, you may find triangular sharks' teeth
at Abbey Wood, near London, though you will fare better in
the sandy beds of the same series. The development of Bony
Fishes increased rapidly, and in Oligocene days they were the
dominant type. Near Osborne in the Isle of Wight there is a clay
bed full of the remains of a small sprat-like fish. The East
Anglian "crags" are even more recent, but the fish remains found
in them often belong to older beds.

In modern times the Ganoids were reduced to a mere handful
of species; the Dipnoi, or Lung-fishes, even fewer; the Selachians
(Sharks and Rays) are still quite numerous, but the Teleostei or
Bony Fishes represent the great majority of fishes, both as species
and individuals.

2

GENERAL ANATOMY

FISHES live and move in water, which is a medium far denser than air. A streamlined body that will allow them freedom of movement is an obvious necessity for them. Streamlining is found everywhere in nature, with countless changes of form adapted to the different functions of the various forms of life, changes that vary between the portly rotundity of the Angler, the slim elongation of the Eel and the flatness of the Sole.

It follows naturally that the internal and external organs of fishes show very wide variations, which can be treated adequately only in a large and specialized textbook. We shall pay more attention to the external appearance, as this is of greater practical importance to our readers.

SKELETON (see Fig. 1). Fishes are *vertebrates*; that is, they have a jointed backbone which, with the rest of the skeleton, supports and strengthens the body. The skeleton is composed of cartilage (gristle) in the Shark, Skate and Lamprey families; in all other fishes it is entirely (or almost entirely) of true bone. The backbone almost always consists of a series of hollow or cup-shaped joints or "vertebrae," connected by ligaments, the hollows filled with a stiff jelly acting as a kind of ball-and-socket joint. In this way the backbone acquires that great flexibility characteristic of fishes. Above the body of the vertebrae there is a *neural arch*, for the passage of the spinal cord, and a spine. Below the vertebrae there are other spines, forming an arch for the passage of large blood-vessels. The ribs, unlike those of mammals, do not enclose the important organs of the chest and do not join in front to form a breastbone. The skull is formed of many bones, for the protection of the brain and of the gills. Fish have never more than two pairs of limbs (fins), and sometimes have less (*e.g.*, Eel). In front are the *pectoral fins*, attached to a structure connected either to the skull or to the backbone. The pelvic or ventral fins,

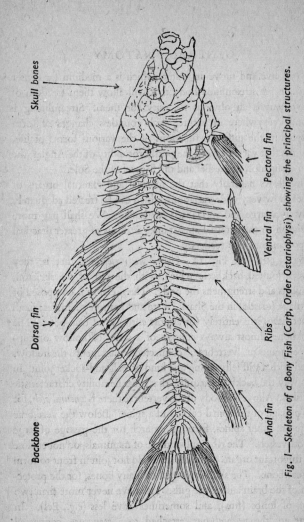

Skull bones

Pectoral fin

Ventral fin

Ribs

Dorsal fin

Anal fin

Backbone

Fig. I.—Skeleton of a Bony Fish (Carp, Order Ostariophysi), showing the principal structures.

when present, are joined together by an arch which is never connected with the backbone. The ventral fins vary in position; they are normally behind the pectorals (*e.g.*, Carp), and in this case the arch is simply fixed inside the muscles of the abdomen. In other cases the ventral fins are just beneath (*e.g.*, Perch) or even in front of the pectorals (*e.g.*, Cod), in which case the ventral arch may be attached to part of the pectoral system.

There are also bones supporting the "unpaired fins," that is, the fins placed on the median line of the body, on the back (dorsal) and the belly (anal). These bones ("interspinous") are a series of sharp spines embedded between the two thick muscular layers forming the flesh of the fish; the inner ends of these bones are connected to the upper spines of the backbone.

FINS (see Fig. 2). The number, size, position and colour of the fins vary so much from fish to fish that they constitute one of the easiest and most important items in identifying fishes. The fins are usually formed of series of thin bones supporting a screen of skin. These bones may be stiff undivided and pointed rods, and are then called *spines*, such as form the first dorsal fin of the Perch; or they may be soft and branched, when they are called *rays* or *branched rays*, as found in the fins of the Herring or of the Roach. Many fishes have both spines and rays, sometimes in the same fin (*e.g.*, the dorsal fin of the Goldfish), sometimes in separate fins (Perch, Mackerel). The Salmon family (and others) have a small fatty dorsal fin, without spines or rays, placed a little before the tail (adipose fin). Sometimes the fins are reduced to spines without skin (Stickleback).

All fishes have at least some trace of a dorsal fin, a fact which points to its importance. The unpaired fins (dorsal and anal) are used mostly as keels to keep the fish upright, especially when not in rapid motion. Fast swimmers, like the Tunny or Mackerel, fold the dorsal fins in a special groove when swimming at high speed, reducing water resistance to a minimum.

There may be one dorsal fin (Carp family, Herring, Pike), two (Perch, Grey Mullets, Salmon family) or three (Cod, Haddock,

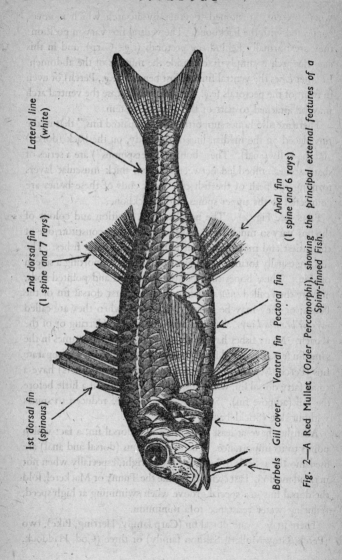

Lateral line (white)

2nd dorsal fin (1 spine and 7 rays)

1st dorsal fin (spinous)

Anal fin (1 spine and 6 rays)

Pectoral fin

Ventral fin

Gill cover

Barbels

Fig. 2—A Red Mullet (Order Percomorphi), showing the principal external features of a Spiny-finned Fish.

Pollack). There may be two dorsal fins, one of stiff spines and one of soft rays, joined together (Ruff, Wrasses), and sometimes a fin may be divided into numerous finlets (Mackerel). Occasionally the dorsal fin joins the caudal (or tail) fin and the anal (Eel), or runs along practically the whole back (Flatfishes, Blennies).

The pelvic (term preferred by biologists) or ventral (term preferred by anglers) fins are sometimes missing (Eel, Wolf-fish, Seahorse), or are modified into suckers (Sucker Fishes) or spines (Stickleback). Their position varies very much; they may be situated on the throat, in front of the pectoral fins (*jugular*; Cod family), on the chest, more or less under the pectorals (*thoracic*; Perch), or on the belly (*abdominal*; Carp family).

The pectoral fins vary a great deal in size and shape, reaching exaggerated developments in the Skates and Flying-fishes. Their position instead remains uniformly behind the gills, though in Skates they spread almost from the snout to the beginning of the tail.

SKIN. Most fishes are covered with scales. These may be *cycloid* (thin, horny, more or less rounded, with fine concentric rings, *e.g.*, Pike, Carp family, Herring, Cod family); *ctenoid* (also thin and flexible, occasionally spiny, firmly fixed into the skin, with a series of comb-like teeth on the free edge, *e.g.*, Perch, Megrim); *placoid* (detached little bony plates with an enamel surface, often armed with spines, typical of the Shark and Skate families); *ganoid* (thick, large bony plates with sharp edges, *e.g.*, Sturgeon). Generally speaking, soft-finned fishes have smooth cycloid scales, and spiny-finned fishes have rough ctenoid scales. Some species may have both (the Dab has spiny scales on the upper side, smooth ones on the lower). In some fishes the scales are partially or totally modified into spines (Porcupine-fishes), bony knobs or tubercles (Turbot), little shields or scutes (Stickleback, Horse Mackerel), or hard plates (Trunk-fishes). The skin is protected by a layer of slime in addition to the scales. Terrestrial animals undergo changes of their outer surface that free them of parasites or supply them with better protection against alterations of climate or of living conditions; thus snakes slough their skins, birds and mammals moult; the epidermis is constantly shed in minute dead flakes and as constantly renewed. The scales of fishes are a permanent protection lasting through life, and they are not shed; the layer of slime fulfils the additional measure of protection of the epidermis. Parasites or fungus spores that attach themselves to a fish are engulfed by the slime and subsequently drop off. It is only when the solid protection of the scales is missing that infections have a chance to get a hold. The wounded fish that has lost some scales may be attacked by a fungus that will cover first the wound, and later on the fish, with a white mildew. It is therefore necessary that anglers should take care to handle very gently a fish they intend to return to the water.

Many fishes have a line along their side from the gill-cover to the middle of the tail; this "lateral line" is an important sense organ (see page 28) and also a very useful means of identifying species by counting the scales along it. The number of scales does not change during the life of a fish; they grow in size with its growth, and in many cases a microscopical examination of the scales may yield important data on the fish's life. A small number of fishes are without scales (Bullheads, Conger, "Leather" Carp), but the Eel is not one of them.

The MOUTH is usually more or less at the end of the snout, but it is occasionally much below, as in Sharks and Skates. In most cases it is provided with teeth, and these show a very great variety in shape and position. In Sharks they are rows of enlarged "placoid" scales on the edge of the jaws; Pike and Trout have teeth covering practically the whole lining of the mouth, including the tongue; the Wolf-fish has a complete collection of powerful teeth of all shapes, that allow it to bite through a lobster and crush the thickest whelks. Fishes of the Carp family have a toothless mouth, but have a few teeth in their throat which bite against a hard plate and help in breaking up their food (normally vegetable). Predaceous fishes have a larger mouth than the others.

Those which feed at the bottom are often supplied with barbels on their lips, serving as sensitive feelers when seeking food (*e.g.*, Carp, Gudgeon, Cod, Pouting). The mouth is also continually taking in gulps of water, which is forced through the breathing apparatus.

RESPIRATION is carried out by means of the *gills*, which vary a good deal, but can be roughly described as series of layers of a thin-skinned frilly tissue, very rich in blood-vessels. The water taken in the mouth passes over the gills, where the oxygen it contains is absorbed by the blood through the thin membrane of

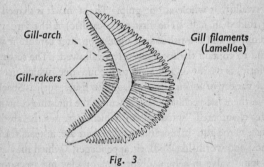

Gill-arch

Gill filaments (Lamellae)

Gill-rakers

Fig. 3

the gills; the water is then ejected through a series of "gill-slits," either directly to the outside (Sharks and Rays) or into a gill-chamber that has a single opening protected by a set of flat bones forming the *gill-cover* (all bony fishes). The gill-slits are nearly always on the side of the neck (in Skates they are under the body, and water is drawn in through a "spiracle" near the eye, often mistakenly believed to be the ear). Inside the mouth the gills are often protected by *gill-rakers* (see Fig. 3)—comb-like structures that strain the water and prevent food or solid particles from escaping. Fish do not need the large amount of oxygen required by warm-blooded animals. The active species can live only in well-oxygenated water, but sluggish types like the Tench can thrive in ponds where a Trout would quickly die. A well-aerated water, such as a mill or weir stream, will be frequented by fish out of condition after spawning, because the extra oxygen will accelerate their functions. Fishes die when taken out of the water because their delicate gills dry up; but fish with small gill openings and well supplied with slime (Eel, Carp) will keep their gills moist and thus resist asphyxia for a long time.

DIGESTIVE SYSTEM. As the breathing is performed by the gills, fishes have no windpipe and only the gullet or oesophagus leads from the mouth into the body cavity. It is capable of stretching considerably, for fishes, as a rule, do not chew their food but swallow it whole at one gulp. The stomach is shaped like a bag folded in half. The first half (cardiac) is the larger; it is distensible, and if a fish is split open soon after capture it will be found to contain the food recently swallowed. The second half (pyloric) is narrower and leads to the intestine, which presents a great variety of forms. In cartilaginous fishes, such as Sharks and Rays, there is a peculiar enlargement of the intestine containing a many-chambered "spiral valve" which increases the absorptive surface of the gut. In most bony fishes there are, instead, from 1 to almost 200 worm-like "pyloric appendages," which may act like the spiral valve in helping absorption, or they may secrete juices aiding digestion. They are very numerous, for instance, in fish of the Salmon family. The length of the intestine varies a lot: Grey Mullets, mostly vegetarian, have an intestinal tube about six times the length of the fish, while in the carnivorous Pike it is as long as the fish. The liver is usually conspicuous, and in some fishes (Cod family, Sharks) it is very large and rich in oil.

BLOOD CIRCULATION in fishes is rather peculiar. In nearly all cases the heart consists of only two cavities (one auricle and one ventricle), as compared with two auricles and one ventricle in amphibians and reptiles, two auricles and two ventricles in birds and mammals. The spent blood from the veins is pumped to the gills, where it absorbs oxygen and is returned to the tissues through the arteries without going back to the heart, as happens in all other vertebrates. The amount of blood is generally less than 2 per cent. of the weight of the fish (a much smaller proportion than in birds or mammals). In consequence of these two facts, circulation is slow, as anybody can notice when a fish is wounded in the gills: the blood, instead of spurting quickly, oozes out slowly. The blood is red (except in the larval young of the Eels, where it is colourless) through the presence of red corpuscles, as is the case in all vertebrates. These corpuscles, unlike those of mammals, are oval and have a nucleus (only the Lampreys have round corpuscles), their size varying a good deal in different species and in consequence their number per cubic inch. In most fishes the blood is at the same temperature as the surrounding water, and a sudden change in temperature may even kill a fish. It has often been stated that a few active fishes have blood at a slightly higher temperature than their surroundings (e.g., Mackerel family). As the bodily processes are made more active by warmth, cold-blooded animals, as a rule, become more lively when their surroundings are warm, and anglers know that many fishes in winter become sluggish or hide away in the mud during the cold season.

Many fishes have a "swim" or "air-bladder" filled with gases (mainly nitrogen in fresh-water fishes, oxygen in sea fishes), whose chief use is probably to regulate the buoyancy of the animal and its internal pressure, but it serves also in the small group of the Lung-fishes (Dipnoi) as an additional breathing organ. Sharks and Rays have no air-bladder.

The KIDNEYS are, as a rule, large and flattened organs behind the swim-bladder, of a dark colour, more or less hidden behind the genital organs or roes. The kidney in fishes has to be very efficient, as it has to regulate the amount of water and salts needed by them. This function will be explained in greater detail in another chapter.

The REPRODUCTIVE ORGANS are generally long, paired structures that become greatly swollen in the spawning season. The females of the Shark group have only one ovary or roe with few eggs in different stages of maturity. Most other fishes have ovaries with compact masses of eggs ripening more or less at the same time. The vent or *cloaca* in fishes represents the opening for the alimentary, genital and excretory systems.

SPECIAL ORGANS. *Electricity*. A few species belonging to various groups are capable of generating electricity, and use it to give electric shocks either to their prey or to their enemies. In Europe the best-known electric fish is the Torpedo, a kind of Ray occasionally caught in British waters. Other species with the same peculiarity are the Electric Catfish, the so-called Electric Eel and the Star Gazer. The shock may be fairly strong and unpleasant, but it is not dangerous to man.

Poison. A great many fishes have sharp spines or edges, with which they can inflict disagreeable pricks or wounds. A few of them have poison organs, more or less virulent, to reinforce their weapons of defence. Here, too, these species belong to widely separated groups. In our islands the most feared are the two Weevers found on sandy shores, where they stay half buried in the sand waiting for shrimps or small fry; the unfortunate bather who steps on a Weever will suffer agonizing pains for several hours (there are cases of children dying from this poisoning). The Piked or Spur Dogfish is less poisonous, but it may inflict larger wounds; the Sting Ray may inflict painful ragged wounds by means of a saw-edged sting hidden in its whip-like tail. Several species with poisonous spines are found in other parts of the world (Catfishes, Sharks, Scorpion-fishes and Toad-fishes). Of our poison fishes it may be useful to remember that the spines of the Spur Dogfish are in front of the two dorsal fins, and that the Weevers' poison organs consist of the black spines of the first dorsal fin and of a spine on each gill-cover. Once the poison organs have been removed, the Weevers are very good eating. The best cure for the wounds caused by poisonous spines consists in the injection of a 5 per cent. solution of potassium permanganate or Condy's Fluid into the wound; a hypochlorite solution (Milton, dilute Javelle water or bleaching powder in water) is also useful. Do not disregard any scratch or small wound caused by the spines or teeth of any fish, as, possibly on account of the slime that covers fishes, it may easily fester. Therefore suck clean the scratch and apply a little disinfectant, even if it is only a drop of the methylated spirit of your lamp.

There are a few species with poisonous flesh (Globe-fishes, Trigger-fishes) and others that may occasionally become poisonous on account of their diet. None of them is British; among our fishes only the Barbel may cause discomfort, as its roes, especially in the spawning season, are a violent purge and emetic.

Light. Many species, especially in very deep water, are supplied with light-organs, giving off a more or less intense phosphorescence, due to the slime secreted by special cells. The light may vary from a dull glow on the whole surface of the fish, or peculiar patterns of spots and lines, to fairly powerful "headlights."

3

BRAIN AND SENSE ORGANS

FISH may have a longer genealogy than any Irish or Scottish family, and be the most numerous of the Vertebrates, but not even their most devoted champion can credit them with much brain. Günther states that the brain of the Burbot is about $\frac{1}{720}$ of the weight of the fish; the proportion is about the same even among the members of the Carp family, in spite of their alertness. In the Pike the proportion falls sharply to $\frac{1}{1300}$, and is even lower among the Sharks; but, as Fabre said, the job of the killer requires no brains. Small as it is, the brain does not fill the whole cavity of the skull, and jelly and fat occupy the space left. It has been observed that the brain does not grow at the same rate as the rest of the body, so that a fish much larger than another of the same species may have only a slightly bigger brain.

Not only the intelligence of fish but their whole nervous system is less developed than that of the higher vertebrates. Their sensitivity is also of a much lower order, and their feelings, both physical and mental, less acute. Their sense of pain is slight, though it does exist. Some anglers are unaware of this fact, possibly because a fish cannot cry out in pain, and its helpless flapping seems merely ridiculous. Their emotions (fear, hope, suspicion) are short-lived and superficial; the Dace that has escaped the jaws of a Pike forgets about it in a few minutes.

This does not exclude a rudimentary individuality in fishes. Anyone who studies fish in an aquarium soon observes differences in behaviour among his specimens, even of the same species and size. We begin to see among fish the first glimpses of "personality," that great faculty which in the highest vertebrate, Man, was placed by St. Thomas Aquinas as the first and greatest gift of God.

The sense organs of fishes are rather peculiar; some of them still remain obscure, so that here is a fruitful field for the observer.

SIGHT. The eye in fishes is rather flattened and is covered by a transparent skin. Only a few Sharks have a kind of eyelid.

It is impossible to see farther than about 10 yards in even the clearest water; the eyes of fishes are therefore adapted for seeing only at short distances. Their optical equipment is of a primitive nature and is quite inefficient for vision beyond a few feet. Fish can see in air, but the peculiar effect of the passage of light through more than one medium (air *and* water) gives rise to rather complicated phenomena of refraction which cannot be discussed here. It will be sufficient to say that fishes see above them only a restricted circular clear zone, whose extent depends on the depth at which the fish lies; the greater the depth the larger the diameter of this circular window on the aerial world. Outside this sphere light is reflected and the fish sees a dark mirroring of the bottom.

I shall be very cautious on the question whether fishes are sensitive to colours. It is probable that some of them, at least, have the capacity for distinguishing some colours. On one side we have biologists who incline to the opinion that fishes are colour-blind; on the other countless anglers dyeing maggots with the greatest care or calculating the most delicate hues for artificial flies as if trout were rivals of the Venetian School of painting in their fastidious and skilful choice of colours. Manufacturers of artificial bait are most solidly of the second opinion; and while biologists are always scientifically doubtful, anglers and tackle makers are aggressively convinced that they are right.

HEARING. Fishes have no external ear and the internal ear is very simplified. Until recently fishes were believed to be deaf, but careful experiments have shown that they can detect sounds, apart from vibrations. Near many ponds there have been, and are, bells which when rung attracted fishes; it was subsequently observed that it was really the sight of people going to throw food to them that attracted the fish, and not the sound. They cannot, however, hear very clearly, and are, as a rule, indifferent to aerial noises that convey no sense of danger to them. Anglers can indulge in conversation freely without fear of frightening their quarry, who are more likely to be alarmed by vibrations transmitted to the water, such as walking heavily on the bank or knocking a pipe on the gunwale of the boat.

SMELL. Except in Lampreys (which are not, strictly speaking, fishes), the nostrils are not connected with the mouth or throat. They lead to a double hollow lined with a sensitive membrane connected with the olfactory nerve. Some fishes, such as Sharks, have a very acute sense of smell and react easily to some odours.

TASTE. As we have already seen, fishes usually gulp their food without chewing it, so that their sense of taste cannot be very highly developed. Some fishes have taste nerves in their mouths, on their palate and lips. The members of the Carp family have teeth in their throat that can crush their food in such a way as to impart its flavour to the taste organs. Some fishes may also taste their prospective food by means of barbels or wattles near their mouths.

BALANCE. The ears of fishes contain small "otoliths" or ear-stones—little white "pebbles" that often puzzle people who cut the heads of large fish for the table. These ear-stones are contained in little sacs forming organs that endow the fish with the power of balancing the body. These otoliths grow from year to year, and may give a clue to the age of the fish.

TOUCH. Fishes have the sense of touch all over their skin, but it is particularly developed in the barbels that are to be found round the mouths of some species, in numbers from one to six (Cod and Ling, one; Tench and Gudgeon, two; Burbot, three; Carp and Barbel, four; Five-bearded Rockling, five; Loaches, six). These fishes are bottom feeders, and their barbels are delicate organs of touch (and maybe of taste) revealing the presence of food.

LATERAL LINE. The majority of fishes have a more or less complete line running along the sides of their bodies from their gills to the tail (the Herring family is a notable exception) which acts as an organ for detecting variations of pressure. The scales on this line are perforated, and cover a canal filled with slime and containing sense cells. When the fish swims in the neighbourhood of some solid object, there is a very slight increase of pressure that is perceived through the lateral line and enables the animal to change its course even in the dark. It also registers the presence of currents and of movements or vibrations in the water, and may give sensations of temperature as well. It is difficult to convey an idea of this sense, because it is entirely lacking in human beings.

4

CLASSIFICATION AND NOMENCLATURE

(BROTHER TAXONOMIST, please be gentle and understanding. This chapter is shameful, I know. Do not forget that there are probably only two or three of my readers in a thousand who know anything about Weberian ossicles, and are not horrified, as they well might be, by such words as hyomandibular or meta-pterygoid. What good would it be to tell anybody, except you who know already, that the cutaneous branch of the trigeminal is typical of the Neopterygii? Skip this chapter, please.)

The classification of fishes is mostly founded on internal anatomical points which, though very important, require a great deal of specialized knowledge and dissecting skill, such as are found only in a few people. Birds and mammals can be easily classified by external features; a glance at their mouths immediately discloses the difference between the similar shrew and mouse, and why they belong to different Orders. Only an expert dissection could reveal the anatomical differences between a Sprat and a Bleak.

I shall have to group fishes in a very "practical" way, ignoring not only small differences but also whole Orders that include species more or less unknown to readers in the British Isles.

(I) *Class* CYCLOSTOMES or *Round-mouths*. Snake-like—a round funnel-like mouth without jaws—a much-reduced gristly skeleton without ribs or joints supporting the fins—breathe by means of a set of pouch-like gills usually showing externally by a row of small slits—no scales or paired fins—more or less parasitic. The best-known members are the Lampreys and the Hag-fish.

(II) *Class* SELACHIANS. Well-developed skeleton made ex-clusively of gristle (cartilage)—several gill-clefts for the passage of the water used for breathing—paired fins—body covered by a tough skin into which are embedded numerous "placoid" scales—

no air-bladder—intestine consisting mostly of a spindle-shaped "spiral valve"—the males have the ventral fins adapted as "claspers." The Selachians are divided into two large sections and a small one.

(a) *Sharks*. Body elongate—gill-slits on side of "neck."

(b) *Rays* or *Skates*. Body flattened—pectoral fins immensely wide—gill-slits under body.

(c) *Rabbit-fishes*. Gill-slits in a chamber, with a single opening outside.

(III) *Class* BONY FISHES. Skeleton more or less formed of true bone—gills protected by a gill-cover opening externally with a single cleft—paired limbs—usually an air-bladder—skin normally covered with scales.

There are a few small sections of this class, that we may call *Ganoids*, which are intermediate between the gristle fishes and the bony fishes. They retain, for instance, the spiral valve, or a certain amount of gristle in their skeleton, or hard ganoid plates instead of thin scales. The Sturgeon is the best-known example.

The typical Bony Fishes (Teleostei or, more modernly, Neopterygii) form by far the largest section. We shall start grouping them by following the old-fashioned method of separating the Orders with soft fins from those with spiny fins.

(a) The SOFT-FINNED FISHES constitute the majority of freshwater species. Their fins are supported by soft rays, though exceptionally there may be one or two spines at the beginning of the dorsal and anal fins. Their scales are usually cycloid.

(i) *Isospondyli*. Air-bladder connected with the gullet by means of a tube—the ventral fins are "abdominal" (placed on the belly)—principal dorsal fin roughly above the ventrals. The Salmon family (with a small "adipose" fin after the normal dorsal fin) and the Herring family (without lateral line) belong to this Order.

(ii) *Haplomi*. A small Order which includes the Pike. Dorsal fin above the anal.

(iii) *Apodes*. No ventral fins—body snake-like—small gill-cleft—peculiar larva shaped like a narrow leaf (leptocephalus). Includes all true Eels.

(iv) *Ostariophysi*. A very large Order with about 5,000 species mostly inhabitants of fresh water. Resemble the Isospondyli, but their air-bladder communicates with the inner ear by means of a set of small bones. Most of its species are grouped in the two sub-orders of the Catfishes and of the Carp-like fishes. This second sub-order accounts for such well-known species as the Roach, Chub, Minnow, etc.

(v) *Synentognathi*. Air-bladder without a duct—ventral fins abdominal—the lateral line is on the lower side of the body and sticks out like a small ridge. The Garfish and the Flying-fishes belong to this Order.

(vi) None of the little *Microcyprini* or Cyprinodonts is a British native species, but many of them are favourite aquarium pets, their smallness, beauty, liveliness and hardihood making them easy and pleasant to keep. The Swordtail, Gambusia, "Millions" and Zebra-fish are often seen in aquaria.

(vii) *Anacanthini*. Extensive soft fins—dull colours—large mouths with numerous teeth—ventral fins jugular (on the throat) —large liver full of oil. The Cod family belongs to this Order.

(viii) *Solenichthyes*. Small odd-looking fishes (such as the Pipe-fishes and the Sea-horse) with a small mouth at the end of a tube-like snout.

There are a few other Orders of soft-finned fishes, none of any particular interest to the British public, such as Gulpers, Lantern-fishes, Trout-perches, Deal-fishes, all inhabitants of the depths of the ocean or of tropical waters.

(*b*) SPINY-FINNED FISHES.

(i) *Percomorphi* or Perch-like. Ventral fins on the chest (thoracic)—first dorsal (or first part of dorsal system of fins) supported by spines—spines often at beginning of ventral and anal fins. This large Order includes the freshwater and marine Perches, Grey Mullets, Sea Breams, Gobies, Blennies, Wrasses, Mackerels, Tunnies, Sword-fishes and the Cichlids.

(ii) *Scleroparei*. Rather similar to the Percomorphi, but distinguished by their "mailed cheeks," as Norman aptly calls them. The Sea-scorpions, Gurnards, Lumpsuckers, Bullheads and also the Sticklebacks are put in this Order.

(iii) *Heterosomata* or Flatfish. Flattened laterally (unlike the Rays, flattened from above) and swimming on one side—fringe of fins on the outline of the body—one side only deeply coloured (both eyes on this side). The Halibut, Turbot, Plaice, Flounder and Sole are well-known members of this Order.

Less important Orders include the John Dories, Trunk-fishes, Puffers, Angler-fishes and a few little-known other groups.

(c) DIPNOI or Lung-fishes.

Air-bladder developed so as to act as a lung, enabling the fish to use atmospheric air for respiration. Fins having a greater resemblance to legs than in any other group of fishes. In anatomy and evolution they form a connecting-link with the amphibians (frogs and newts). The few existing species live in Central Africa, South America and Australia.

NOMENCLATURE. It is generally believed that calling a spade a spade helps towards clarity and understanding. It is most regrettable that such a course is not possible when mentioning fishes. The confusion of names is so great, even in one tongue, that long ago naturalists tried to fix a Latin name and surname (even a nickname) on every animal and plant. The surname is common to several species of the same little group or *genus*, and several little groups or *genera* make a family. Every species has its name, and a kind of nickname may be given to varieties of one species. For instance, the Salmon belongs to the genus *Salmo* of the family Salmonidae; as a species it is called *salar*. The group (genus) name goes first, with a capital initial, the species name goes second, with a small initial. Final result: *Salmo salar*, the Salmon. Scientific books also give the name or initial of the first naturalist who described or classified the animal or plant.

Most unfortunately, for reasons that would take too long to

discuss here, there is not yet a general agreement about these scientific or systematic labels. The names I have given are those generally recognized at the present time, but I do not expect them to tally entirely with the names you will find in other books.

The confusion of scientific names is nothing in comparison with the joyous chaos of the local names. Longshoremen have a wonderfully poetic imagination when it comes to christening specimens caught by their customers, and I suspect that it is on such a basis that the guide-book of a great railway company lists three species of Conger (there is only one). Fish often have different names for every stage of their growth (Salmon, Cod), and these names vary from one district to another. Day gives over fifty different names for the Coalfish (*Gadus virens* or *carbonarius*) in British waters alone. The fish trade, hoping that a Dogfish under another name might smell sweeter and sell more easily, calls it "flake." The name of "rock salmon," given impartially by fishermen to the Coalfish and the Wolf-fish (also called Catfish), extends its scope in the fried-fish shop to include any fish of ungainly appearance or unappetizing reputation or whose name is unknown to the fishmonger and to the public. Quite rightly, too, if this is the only way to get a conservative public to eat and enjoy wholesome and tasty fish that would otherwise be shunned because its name is unknown.

I have given, therefore, the principal and most widespread names, and the reader must try to find out the identity of the species or specimen that interests him from the description given rather than from the names he may hear. One name often embraces several different species, while, on the other hand, the same species in the same district may be known by a variety of names. A *joey* is a small Mackerel, a *smolt* a young Salmon (or Sea Trout), a *bream flat* a small Bronze or Silver Bream.

Do not blame your textbooks if they do not mention the name you have been told on the jetty or in the dinghy you have hired; most probably that name will be forgotten within an hour by the man who told you.

5

REPRODUCTION

FISHES in general reproduce their kind once in a year. There is, otherwise, no sort of uniformity in their breeding habits, nor in the incidence or duration of their spawning seasons. It often happens that fishes of the same family, inhabiting neighbouring territories, breed at roughly the same time, but there is no hard-and-fast rule in the matter, popular tradition notwithstanding. (The Salmon family provides us with one noteworthy instance, in that while the Grayling spawns in spring, the Salmon, the Trout and the Chars spawn in autumn and winter.) Generalizations, here as in other places, are liable to be misleading.

In the breeding season the males of many species show peculiar secondary sexual characters. These may be represented by unusual and brighter colours, such as displayed by the Chars, the Lumpsucker, the Wrasses and the Stickleback. (This last well-known little fish assumes in the spring a vivid red colour on his throat that is not seen at other times.) Or they may take the form of physical changes; as, for example, the hooked lower jaw of the Salmon, the little warts on the head of members of the Carp family, the rows of white tubercles of the Houting, or the lengthened fin rays of the Dragonet.

Fish usually congregate on well-defined spawning grounds, and this causes migrations that vary from a few yards in the case of some freshwater fishes to the thousands of miles of the Eels. Some fishes will seek shallow water (Salmon, Carp, Pike, Gobies), others the deepest (Eels) ; some will come close to the shore (Sand-eels, Smelt), others will go far away (Flounder, Pilchard). "Anadromous" fishes leave the sea to spawn in fresh water (Salmon, Shads, Lampreys) ; "catadromous" fishes descend from fresh water to the sea to spawn (Eel). Fish that are normally solitary (Salmon, Pike, Bullhead) pair off and some may go to considerable trouble for the sake of their brood ; while shoal fish

(Cod, Bream, Herring) congregate and lay their spawn indiscriminately, without any care for the offspring.

Internal fertilization is rare among bony fishes but is the rule among cartilaginous (gristly) fishes, such as Sharks and Skates. Normally the female lays the eggs and the male fertilizes them with his milt. The majority of sea fishes lay "pelagic" eggs, very small, often with a minute oil drop, which float and come to the surface, sometimes in such incredible numbers as to impart a cloudy appearance to vast stretches of the sea. There, in the warmer layers, exposed to light, air and the heat of the sun, these eggs hatch quickly. Young larval fishes are very delicate, and changes of temperature may destroy them by the million in a few hours. This method of procreation is very wasteful, and the fish that have adopted it must lay eggs in enormous quantities if their species is to survive. Thus we have some members of the Cod family, e.g., the Ling (the most prolific of all fishes), the Cod and the Hake, or a flatfish like the Turbot, that lay several million eggs; a large Ling may easily lay 30 millions in a season.

Most freshwater fishes (and some sea fishes) have eggs that are either moored to the bottom by means of tendrils (Dogfish, Garfish), strips of jelly (Perch) or a sticky surface (Herring, Chub, Pike), or that remain at the bottom because they are heavier than water (Salmon family). This kind of egg (demersal) is often laid in much smaller quantities. A 20-lb. Salmon may have about 17,000 eggs, while a Cod of the same size will have more than 6 millions. Demersal eggs are usually larger; e.g., the eggs of the Salmon and of the Wolf-fish are about a quarter of an inch in diameter, while the pelagic egg of the Ling is only one-twenty-fifth.

Except in fresh water, fish very seldom form hybrids. Freshwater hybrids will be described in the sections for the Perch and Carp families.

COURTSHIP AND BROOD CARE. Courtship, general among birds, is uncommon among fish. Only a few among those which lay demersal (bottom) eggs have some form of courtship, though quite a number assume special colorations during the breeding season. In practically all cases courtship ends with the laying of the eggs. Once this has happened, the female takes no further interest in her offspring, and the male is too taken up with looking after the eggs to continue courtship. Brood care in fishes is almost exclusively carried out by the males.

The Sticklebacks, found practically everywhere and known to all boys, are perhaps the best example. In the spring the male assumes a vivid livery with red underparts. He builds a round nest, lacing together fine straws and grasses with the fronds of water weeds, binding these materials with sticky threads secreted by his kidneys. Once the nest is made, he flaunts his bright colours before a female, until he induces her to lay some eggs in the nest. These he fertilizes immediately, and repeats his courtship with other females, until the nest harbours a sufficient number of eggs. Then he mounts guard, forcing a current of water over them by fanning his pectoral fins. The eggs hatch out from 8 to 12 days later, and the father keeps the fry inside the nest for about a month, until they can fend for themselves. During this time he protects his brood with the greatest pugnacity.

The little Gobies, common in rock pools at low tide, also display brighter colours at the breeding season. The male chooses a suitable spot for the eggs, such as an empty shell or a crack in the rocks, and then proceeds to secure a mate by displaying his bright coloration and by fighting rivals. Mating takes place and the eggs are laid ; the female leaves them to the care of the father, who guards them most anxiously until they are hatched, defending them with the utmost gallantry.

A fish with pelagic (floating) eggs, the Dragonet, also favours courting, the male displaying his brilliant colours and long fins to the females to secure their affection. There is no brood care. The Wrasses of our rocky shores make a rough nest of seaweed on which the eggs are deposited. The male Lumpsucker guards his brood even when it is left stranded on the shore by the tide. The Blennies curl themselves round their cluster of eggs; one of them, the Butterfish of our rock pools, shares the care of the eggs with the female, a rather uncommon case. Male Pipefishes and Seahorses have peculiar pouches, where the eggs are kept until they hatch out and where the small larvae are sheltered for some time. Other fish content themselves with scooping a hollow in the sand or gravel, depositing the eggs there and covering them with the same material (Salmon and Lampreys).

DEVELOPMENT OF THE EGGS. Only a few fishes give birth to living young (e.g., Viviparous Blenny, Norway Haddock, Tope, Spur Dogfish); all the others lay eggs at different seasons. The embryos develop more or less quickly, according to the temperature of the water, the size of the egg, the amount of food contained and the species. Usually the eggs of small-sized fish hatch out more quickly than those of their larger brethren. Small pelagic eggs with little oil or yolk mature more rapidly, but the fry is rather primitive and rudimentary. In most cases the newly hatched fishes are far from resembling their parents, and are to be considered as *larvae*, in more or less the same relation to their progenitors as tadpoles are to frogs.

Temperature regulates the ripening of the eggs, and therefore cold retards hatching. Thus the eggs of Trout and Salmon, though laid in the autumn or winter, hatch out several weeks later in early spring. The eggs of most other freshwater fish are laid in the spring, and hatch out in eight to fifteen days. In this manner the young larvae of different species appear when the warmer climate and the abundant sunlight have multiplied those microscopic forms of life (minute plants like Diatoms and tiny Algae, infinitesimal animalculae, larvae of shellfish and worms, etc.) that serve as food for them.

6

YOUTH AND GROWTH

WE have seen in the chapter on Reproduction that, apart from a small number of species, fishes are hatched from eggs.

The few eggs produced by most Sharks and Rays are large, and have tough cases which act as very effective refuges for the embryos. These embryos develop very slowly, but by the time they leave the shell are already complete replicas of their parents. (You may sometimes find stranded on the shore a "mermaid purse" still containing the young fish, and you will recognize immediately—even apart from the different shape of the case—whether it is a tiny shark or skate.) Once they have left the shell these young fishes, as well as those born viviparously, start an independent existence, seeking their food.

In most other cases the eggs ripen quickly and hatch out in a few days or weeks. The newly hatched fish carries under its body a small bag (yolk-sac) containing the rest of the egg's yolk. At this stage its appearance is rather odd. Though it is obviously an infant fish, it has the exaggerated head and eyes so common among embryos or newly-born higher animals. It has a long body and a long tail bordered all round with a continuous fin; apart from the eyes and specks of pigment, it is colourless and transparent. At this stage of life the larval fish does not feed; it floats and drifts on the surface (if pelagic) or hides in the gravel or cracks of the bottom (if demersal), with a few occasional wrigglings. This period lasts from a few days, in the case of most sea fish and members of the Carp family, to a month or more as in the Salmon, until the yolk-sac has been entirely absorbed and the mouth and stomach are ready to function. Then the minute fry start feeding on the immense variety of almost invisible forms of life floating or crawling about, such as microscopic plants (Algae and Diatoms) and animals (Protozoa), and the eggs and larvae of worms, shellfish, jellyfish, urchins, etc., as well as the eggs and

young of fishes smaller than their species. As happens with the
young of every creature, their activity and appetite are remarkable and their growth rapid.

The very young fish is often vastly different from the adult.
At first they are transparent, and only slowly do their skin and
scales assume the common silvery appearance. The infant Cod has
a small black spot near its tail that disappears later on; Salmon,
Trout and Char have their bodies marked with a set of dark vertical
spots (parr marks); the Flatfish are far from being flat, and they
have one eye on each side of the head, like any other baby fish;
the Swordfish has no sword; the Garfish develops first the lower
jaw in a beak, then the upper one; the Sunfish is covered with
sharp spines, before turning into the big smooth ball of the adult;
the Eels are shaped like a willow leaf; and so on.

Life is full of dangers for larval and young fish. Their incomplete development renders them delicate; the waters that they
inhabit (top layers of sea or shallow water of the shore) are those
most likely to experience wide and sudden changes of temperature and composition. A heavy fall of rain will change the amount
of salt (salinity) in the water to a point unbearable to the feeble
structure of the larvae. A heat wave or a bad night frost will be
disastrous to their weak organisms, while a storm or strong wind
will toss them about and buffet them to death. Their swimming
power is too small to enable them to remove to more sheltered or
suitable surroundings.

They have many enemies. In the plankton of the sea surface,
on the shore, in rivers and ponds small and relatively weak carnivorous animals abound which can prey only on weaker forms.
Very young fish, with a feeble cover of thin scales and skin, unable
to swim quickly and ignorant of dangers, are easy prey, not only
to bigger or older fish, but to sea anemones, jellyfishes, crabs,
crayfish, worms of many kinds and insects such as water scorpions
and boatmen or larvae of dragon-flies and beetles.

It is not surprising that, with all these difficulties to overcome,
so few of the millions of eggs laid by fish like the Ling, the Cod

or the Turbot reach maturity. And if the adults, who alone can perpetuate their species and are protected from dangers, are subject to slaughter by human agencies (either through river pollution or overfishing), it will be even less surprising to hear loud complaints that fish are not so abundant as they used to be. And if Man, guided only by greed and stupidity, persists in his ways, not only fish but many other material and immaterial good things will be threatened with extinction and Mankind with them.

It is during the larval stage that are evolved the permanent characteristics. The larval Flatfish turns one of its eyes from one side of the head to the other and takes to the bottom, where only one side of its body will become coloured. The Eel changes from a flat creature $2\frac{1}{2}$ in. long to a round one not more than 2 in., from leptocephalus to elver. A fixed number of scales forms on the skin, and in most cases this number will not alter: they increase in size only, and their number is a very useful pointer for the identification of species. The long fin that follows a large part of the larval fish's profile is split in several portions or partly disappears. Colour and pattern appear and become progressively those of the adult. The source of food changes, and the young fish finds new surroundings. The shoals of fry may break up, and the small fish live in little groups or adopt a solitary existence. As they grow larger and older, they usually descend to deeper water within their customary surroundings.

And there the fish feeds and grows, as much and as well as it can. Growth is rapid in youth and slow during the adult stage, but it does not stop, as with the majority of animals, when a certain age or stage of development has been reached. If conditions are favourable, food abundant and space plentiful, a maximum and even an exceptional size may be reached, because in such a case a fish keeps growing until it dies. This does not mean that a Minnow will become as big as a Pike: it will only become an exceptionally big Minnow, just as the half-pound Gudgeon in Messrs. Clay's reservoir became giant specimens (see page 159).

But if conditions, food and living space are unfavourable growth stops irrespective of age. The overcrowded little pond will be full of adult Carp or Roach 3 or 4 in. long, or of famished Pike weighing as many ounces as they ought to weigh pounds. Trout anglers know that often one has to choose from streams where there are many small Trout or a few good ones. Remove those dwarf Carp and Roach from their pond, and stock with them an empty one; in a short time those fish will grow to respectable size. "And thereby hangs a tale" for men as for fish.

7

LOCOMOTION

FISHES inhabit a much denser medium than do land animals, and it is a prime necessity with them to have a shape that permits free movement. We shall see in a later chapter in what manner certain individual species adapt themselves to their special circumstances. For the present, however, it will be sufficient to note that the torpedo or spindle shape, in one form or another, predominates, while the flattened leaf-like shape is not uncommon. Both kinds are found in varying degrees of streamlining. (The very word streamlining is derived from this association of ideas.)

Fishes usually get about by swimming; some, but very few, by crawling or burrowing. Flying (more accurately gliding) is very uncommon (Flying-fishes, Flying Gurnard, etc.). Leaping or jumping is merely an occasional accidental result of rapid swimming.

Swimming. We are tempted (by a misleading analogy with our own clumsy attempts at natation) to the assumption that swimming is accomplished by the action of the pectoral fins, whereas in fact the function of these fins is, as a rule, quite secondary. In reality fishes derive their motive power from undulations of their bodies, powerfully supported by the tail and the tail fin. Watch carefully the movements of any elongated fish (Eel, Garfish or even Dogfish), either in its native waters or in an aquarium. The motions are so ample and slow as to be quite unmistakable. In the case of Trout or Whiting or other fast swimmers with shorter bodies, the movements are so slight and quick that the only perceptible motion is that of the tail with its fin, which seems to scull the fish along.

The tail fin fulfils another office—that of acting as a point of leverage whenever the fish wishes to change its course. The spread-out fin gives sufficient resistance to permit the animal to turn. These being the functions of the tail fin, it is not surprising to observe that long, slim fishes (such as Blennies, Eels, Pipefishes) have very often smaller tail fins than their short and stocky brethren (such as Bream, Carp).

The dorsal and anal fins act as stabilizing keels to keep the body erect, and are therefore spread out when the fish is still or moving slowly. The pectoral and ventral fins also act as stabilizers and are used for slow movements; they may occasionally serve as brakes and to help in turning the body.

Flatfishes likewise swim by undulations of their bodies, but keeping them in a horizontal instead of a vertical plane like their spindle-shaped brethren.

In their movements the long fins (really dorsal and anal) on the sides help in the wave motion that propels the fish. Another type of flattened fishes, the Skates, have enormously developed pectoral fins extended to make "wings," which are waved when swimming. All flatfishes can also glide long distances by keeping their bodies stiff.

The pectoral fins are used as swimming organs only for very slow movements, and only a small number of fish that normally rest on the bottom, and move in jerks over short distances, use them as the principal means of locomotion. In these cases the pectorals are much larger than usual. The Bullhead of our streams is a good example, as are the Gobies and Blennies of the rock pools around our coasts.

A few fishes swim by means of rapid vibrations or wavings of their dorsal or anal fins. One of these is the grotesque-looking John Dory; another is the quaint little Seahorse, which seems to be provided with a minute propeller turning rapidly to move the rigid little body of its owner. A similar fashion is adopted by the Pipefishes.

Flying. The Flying-fishes and Flying Gurnard soar and glide in the air with the help of their much-enlarged pectoral fins, after a vigorous swimming effort has succeeded in getting them out of the water.

Crawling. This activity is naturally restricted to fishes living on the bottom, and then only to a section of these. In many cases these fishes swim slowly just above the bottom, using their paired fins. Some of them have their ventral fins modified into a sucker (Lumpsucker, Sea-snail, Suckers) or in a kind of disc that can hold on to stones (Gobies); they anchor themselves to the rocks, moving only occasionally and very slowly, except when making sudden darts after their prey. The best example of true crawling is shown by the Gurnards, whose pectoral fins have the first three rays free. This fish (which in water loses practically all its weight) can "walk" slowly on the bottom with these appendages, as you have perhaps noticed in an aquarium.

Burrowing. Few fishes are true burrowers. The Eel will hide itself in mud, the Sand-eels in sand, but only for temporary protection. The dangerous Weevers bury themselves in sand and wait there for their prey, keeping only their eyes and mouth above the sand and their poisoned spines ready to inflict painful wounds on anyone who might tread on them.

Parasitic Locomotion. The Lampreys and the Remoras are good swimmers, but have organs that allow them to attach themselves to other fishes or even boats and to be transported about. The Remoras have the first dorsal fin adapted as an oval sucker, with which it adheres to Sharks or ships. The Lampreys have a suctorial mouth and a rasping tongue; they fasten themselves to the skin of fishes and rasp away the flesh, feeding on their unfortunate carrier, sometimes until it dies.

Speed. The *Countryman* of spring 1943 gave some swimming speeds, in which the Tunny comes first with 44 miles per hour; the Blue Shark can go at 26·5 m.p.h. Trout have been timed with a stopwatch to make 23·25, with the Salmon a little faster; the dash of a Pike reaches 20·5, while Roach and Perch manage about half that speed.

8

DISTRIBUTION AND ADAPTATION

FISHES are to be found almost everywhere, when the water is not too hot, too salty or poisonous. They have succeeded in adapting themselves to very varied conditions of life, ranging from the tidal waters of the shore to the depths of the oceans, from the icy Arctic and Alpine streams and lakes to the hot, muddy marshes of Central Africa.

Fishes, however, like all "cold-blooded" animals, are much less independent of their surroundings than are the warm-blooded ones. A bird or a mammal has in itself a source of heat that enables it to bear sudden changes of temperature without any great loss of vitality, while similar changes would immediately render torpid or even kill most cold-blooded animals.

Luckily for aquatic animals, water has an exceptionally high capacity for holding heat (its specific heat is taken as a measure for all others), and in consequence its temperature rises or falls very slowly, especially where the sea is deep. Creatures living in shallow waters are better able to withstand wide variations in temperature, such as occur in tidal waters in summer. Offshore, especially in the seas round the British Isles, there is a maximum difference of less than 14° F. between the surface temperature of water in summer and winter. In deep water there is even less variation. When in exceptional years the temperature rises or falls considerably above or below the average, large numbers of aquatic animals, including fish, die. The intense cold killed a large number of fish in the North Sea in February 1929, and probably a similar fate overtook them during the cold winters of 1941 and 1942. An abnormally hot summer may also kill off many fish, either directly or through the destruction of smaller organisms which form their diet.

But although sea water varies only slightly in temperature from summer to winter in a given place, it varies a great deal from one place to another, even within a small area. Cold and warm currents, submarine ridges, headlands, all may cause differences of temperature within a few miles. Different fish prefer different zones of the sea according to the temperature; likewise with fresh waters, especially lakes, but not to such a marked degree. Some fishes have either adopted surroundings with the temperature best suited to them or have adapted themselves to the temperature in which they find themselves. Whichever the case, they generally keep very strictly to the temperature they prefer, when they have any choice. Cod on the Great Banks of Newfoundland abound in water of a certain temperature. The Sailfish cruises in the blue waters of the Gulf Stream near the Florida Coast, and only occasionally leaves the warm current. Between the Shetlands and the Faeroes there is a submarine ridge with sharp slopes, which is an effective barrier to the flow of the slightly warmer Atlantic streams towards the Norwegian coast; the difference in aquatic life on the two sides of this ridge is really remarkable. Big Halibut are found in cold zones, and Cod, Haddock and other valuable fish prefer Arctic or sub-Arctic conditions, and there go in search of them those gallant deep-sea fishermen whose harsh lives and courage are too little known to the public. Some fishes never leave the Tropics, others occasionally leave the warm seas to find the migrating shoals of their victims, such as the Tunny which leaves the Mediterranean to feast on the Herrings of the North Sea. Trout and Char are to be found in Alpine lakes and streams that rival Arctic seas in coldness, while Lung-fish can live in hot mud. Eels thrive in warm lagoons and Alpine streams, while Char keep to the colder parts of cold lakes.

Temperature is, however, only one of the conditions of life. When we consider the other aspects of the surroundings of fishes, we cannot help being struck by the variety of places in which they choose to live, and by the adaptations needed to get the best from them. Let us observe the commonest freshwater fishes, which are the easiest to study. Most of those in Britain belong to the Carp family. In spite of belonging to the same family and of sharing the same restricted habitat, they have specialized in their surroundings and adapted themselves in a remarkably efficient way.

In small rills and streams you will find Loaches and Bullheads hunting on the bottom for small insect larvae and worms, while in the water above Trout and young Salmon (these two in moor or hill streams) snap up flies. The stream becomes a small river and other species appear, such as Dace, Roach, Grayling. Of these the Roach choose the quieter reaches, where their deep bodies will not have to struggle against the current; here they feast on their varied diet of small invertebrates, seeds, water-wee buds and bread. The slim Dace and Grayling prefer the more rapid water, where they can easily catch the insect nymphs and flies struggling in the swirling current; they, like Trout, get more vitality from the better oxygenated running water. If the bottom is muddy we shall find Eels, whose snaky shape, tight gill-covers and smallness of fin enable them to wriggle through the mud and hide in the tangled roots of the overhanging bank. When the river becomes bigger Chub, Perch and Bleak abound. Chub like the vicinity of bushes and trees, hoping for morsels to fall into the water from the leaves; they have a big mouth and a hearty appetite, and are not particular as to what they eat. The Perch prefers quiet reaches, because, like the Roach, it does not want to struggle with its deep body against the current; its favourite habitat is either banks of weeds, snaggy bottoms or camp sheddings, where small fish congregate and can easily be seized in large numbers. In the largest rivers, where the water runs either deep or fast, we find the Barbel, rooting on the bottom; the Bleak darts about near the surface, swallowing flies and gnats; while the Minnow skirts the shallows in search of any small prey, poking its short snout into every new place; the Gudgeon, like a miniature Barbel, goes grubbing on the bottom in the places its bigger brother does not frequent.

In the slow and quietest reaches of rivers you may find other fishes, such as Carp, Tench and Bream, sluggish creatures nosing in the mud for anything that they can swallow. Eels thrive in the estuaries, where tides bring some salt into the river water, and a few species, such as Bass, Flounder and Grey Mullets, enter the stream at high tide; some of them may even swim for miles up the river, where it is quite fresh; for example, Bass are found at Arundel, far from the sea.

Let us pass to lakes, meres and ponds. Conditions may vary greatly, and we may expect to find different fauna in the shallow Broads, deep Cumberland lakes, rocky Scottish lochs and muddy countryside ponds. The food supply is different, both in type and quantity. The abundant growth of vegetation is possible only in shallow water, because fresh water is usually less transparent than sea water, and plants often cannot grow in it at a depth of more than 7 yards. Plentiful vegetation means plenty of food for all kinds of fishes, whether they eat plants, mud or small creatures feeding on vegetable matter. In the deep and clear mountain lakes vegetation is scanty in proportion to the volume of water, and the fish must feed on the rare insect and fish fauna (as Trout and Char do) or on minute floating organisms (animal and vegetable) as the fry or the Whitefish do. On the other side clear mountain lakes are well oxygenated; water at a low temperature holds more dissolved oxygen, and the rills among the boulders absorb much vivifying gas before reaching the lake. Thus this water is ideal for Trout and Char, which both need about 12 cu. in. of oxygen per gallon of water. In shallow muddy ponds the water does not get so well aerated; also the presence of rotting weeds and leaves consumes part of the oxygen in the water. Therefore Salmonids could not live in such surroundings, though some members of the Carp family find them perfectly congenial. Carp, Bream and Tench can live in ponds where the oxygen content of the water is about half that needed by Trout; the mud found there is a useful addition to their diet, even if their flesh absorbs its flavour to the detriment of its culinary value. They prefer the weediest parts of ponds and meres, while the Rudd keeps to the clear water just beyond the banks of reeds.

Thus all the fresh waters of Britain, except those poisoned by the refuse of Blake's "dark satanic mills," have their fish, which have chosen the surroundings they find most congenial. In the mountain stream, leaping like liquid crystal from boulder to boulder, you will find Trout, while the Tench thrives in the slime of the foul ditch by the railway cutting.

THE SEA. The variety of fish life in the seas is infinitely greater, and variations are on a different standard. Here we can distinguish between the top of the water and the bottom, between the shallow and the deep sea; where conditions are uniform, there will be a curious uniformity of fish life; where conditions vary, there we shall find the greatest variety.

The greatest uniformity of colour is found among fishes that live far from the coast (*oceanic*). Only different conditions of temperature and light cause variety. Thus fishes living near the surface are, as a rule, blue on their upper part and white below. Species living between about 100 and 300 fathoms are usually silvery all over and with large eyes; at greater depths the colour is generally uniformly dark; those living in the dark zones of the sea are often supplied with light-organs or *photophores*. It is worth noting that several species of these abyssal fishes are to be found all over the world. Fishes living in the oceanic depths have no source of food other than the animal life around them, which is not too abundant; they have found several ways of solving this all-important problem. Some make nocturnal excursions to the upper layers, where life is more concentrated; others have developed an incredible swallowing capacity, that enables them to make enormous meals when they chance to find a victim. A well-known species, which has deserved the name of Swallower, can succeed in gulping down other fishes much larger than itself, by means of a huge mouth, distensible jaws and a stomach that can be stretched to an enormous extent. Abyssal fishes often have the most nightmarish appearance, with great mouths fitted with long sharp teeth, strange filaments and barbels, misshapen bodies and queer fins, and sometimes rows of lights and huge eyes. These apparent deformities are really adaptations to inhospitable surroundings. The light-organs and the enormous eyes are needed to supply some means of seeing in the darkness. Where sight does not suffice, the barbels and filaments act as sensitive organs of touch and possibly of taste. The big mouths and teeth are needed to make sure that the few meals that are encountered have no chance of escape.

The fishes that inhabit the surface oceanic layers are usually very good swimmers, and they are also predaceous. On the other hand, there are a few, like the Sunfish, who are feeble swimmers and feed on small floating organisms; it is interesting to note that the Sunfish, when young, would be an easy prey to faster-moving enemies if it were not covered with spines; the adult fish, being almost round and very large, is safe from most enemies.

The most interesting variety of forms is to be found near the coasts and in regions where the water is not deeper than 100 to 120 fathoms. This zone seethes with every form of animal and vegetable life.

All animal life is dependent ultimately on plants, which alone are capable of producing their own food, absorbing its elements from air, water and soil. Almost all sea plants are of a primitive kind, and most species are of minute size; they need light to carry out their chemical processes of photosynthesis and salts to build their protoplasm. An excess of light may be harmful; it is well known that ultra-violet rays have a powerful microbicide action, and the minute diatoms of the surface are not much bigger than bacteria. Therefore, if the light is too strong, these tiny plants grow better a few yards below the surface, while in dull light, all of which they need, they grow on the surface. Mineral salts (called "manurial" salts), containing phosphorus, nitrogen, iron, potassium, are carried into the sea by rivers; they are also yielded by animal excreta and by the decomposition of dead animals and plants. This decomposition takes place at the bottom, where there is little or no light; but storms (in moderately shallow water) stir up the lower layers and mix them with the upper ones, thus supplying plants with those elements. These small plants supply food not only to larval fishes but to small animals which form the diet of larger fishes. Thus minute shrimp-like creatures called copepods are the biggest source of food for herrings, and shoals of these fish search the sea for places where these small floating creatures abound. *Plankton* is the name given to all living organisms, animal or vegetable, floating freely in the water.

Let us journey down from the seashore, as we did for rivers. First of all, it may be noted that there are several kinds of shores: there are stern cliffs of hard almost unbroken rock or cliffs consisting of boulders and soft rocks full of cracks; rocky flat shores full of weedy pools at low tide; gravelly, or sandy, or muddy. The shore may be exposed to the great Atlantic rollers or to the gentle tides of an almost landlocked bay. The variety is great, and so is the diversity of forms of life.

Few creatures can live along the exposed cliffs of Northern Cornwall, County Clare or the Western Isles; not even seaweeds can grow there, except in rare clefts. In the bays you may find stretches of good sand, but if these beaches are also exposed to the big waves they will be devoid of invertebrate life (worms, shellfish, shrimps, etc.) and consequently of fish ; the waves stir and fling the sands everywhere, and no animal could live under such conditions. No worm-casts, starfish or shore crabs are to be seen there.

If the cliffs are not so exposed, especially if the rocks are slaty, flaggy or hollowed out, it is quite different. These shores provide plentiful shelter, and cracks, holes and rocky pools are crowded with every kind of seaweed, snail, crustacean, sea anemone, mussel, sea-squirt, sponge, etc. You will find a plentiful assortment of fishes enjoying both the shelter and the abundant food. A closer examination of the species reveals some interesting examples of adaptation. For instance, several of these fishes have an elongated shape which enables them to crawl into holes and cracks (Conger, Rocklings, Blennies); others are of small size, such as would enable them to hide in the weeds or to get into small holes or even shells (Blennies, Pipefishes, Gobies); and some are supplied with suckers that can fix them to rocks or pebbles and resist the action of the waves (Gobies, Suckers).

Little fish life is to be found on gravelly or sandy shores exposed to powerful waves. Pebbles grinding together and deeply shifting sands give seaweeds no chance to anchor themselves firmly to give shelter to small forms of life. If the sandy or gravelly shore is sheltered, and in consequence the bottom is not everlastingly stirred, conditions are quite different. Seaweeds can grow on pebbles, and Seagrass (*Zostera*) can push its roots under the sand and its leaves into the shallow water; cockles, razor-shells, worms of many kinds can burrow underneath, while shrimps, shore crabs and snails crawl on the sand; here you will find such fish as Blennies, Sand-eels and Flatfish, with the roving Bass haunting the surf in search of prey.

The muddy shore is always sheltered; mud consists of very fine particles that can settle only in relatively quiet water; that is, water which is either sheltered or deep. Therefore, on our shores we shall find it in estuaries or in deep bays or havens. Mud is full of small burrowing creatures that attract Flounders and Eels.

Up to now we have observed shallow shores where the tides and the waves exert their power. If we descend to deeper water we can classify fish life according to the bottom, from mud and sand through gravel and pebble to rock. Invertebrate life varies according to the softness or hardness of the bottom, and so do the fish that feed on it.

A soft bottom near the ebb line of spring tides (that is, at the lowest reaches of the lowest possible tides) teems with small creatures. The number of different kinds of worms, sea-urchins, shells (cockles, tellines, clams, etc.), starfishes, sea-cucumbers, crabs, snails, etc., may reach several thousands per square yard, all burrowing at various depths, while shrimps and many crabs crawl on the surface ready to dig themselves in if danger threatens.

This is the favourite residence of most Flatfish (especially Dab, Plaice, Sole, Lemon Sole), of the poisonous Weevers, of Rays, some of the smaller Sharks, Sand-eels, Sand-smelts, Whiting, etc. Other fish are occasionally found, usually good swimmers, like the Mackerel, that can roam about at any depth and on any bottom. The Sand-eels often burrow into the sand above low-water level, and supply castle-building children with the exciting adventure of catching a "baby eel" when least expected.

Rocky or stony bottoms below the tide zone harbour a be-wildering assortment of fishes, which is easily understandable when one considers the wealth of food and protection which they provide. The rocks are covered (to the limit of light penetration) with all kinds of seaweeds, from the green and brown found in shallow water to the bright red which grow in deep water. In the fronds of the weeds countless small creatures find food and refuge; barnacles, sea-squirts, sea-urchins, corals, sea-mats live permanently on the rocks; gastropods (snails, whelks, tower-shells, winkles, limpets—all with only one shell), crustacea (crabs, prawns, crawfish, etc.) and some worms are everlastingly looking for meals in every cranny; lobsters and octopuses lurk in holes; and at every level, but especially near the bottom, we find fish. The big-mouthed members of the Cod family (Pollack, Coalfish, Cod, Ling, Haddock, Pouting) are ready to gulp any-thing from a worm to another fish. The brightly-coloured Wrasses with their powerful teeth are able to nibble off and crush shellfish. The Gurnards creep about on the leg-like separate rays of their pectoral fins. The Sea Breams and the Wolf-fish look for shellfish on the bottom, where Conger, Ling and Rocklings compete with lobsters for comfortable holes. Roaming fish, such as Mackerel and Bass, also swim about in search of prey.

Generally speaking, the farther one goes from the shore the bigger the fish one finds. Every sea fisherman will tell you that if you want to catch really good Plaice or Whiting you must go a few miles from the shore. Naturally this is not a fixed rule, as depth of water and type of bottom are very important factors.

Far from the shore, if the water is very deep, there are the two classes of fishes already mentioned: the abyssal types in the depths and the swift-moving, oceanic types roaming in the upper layers; these often come near the shore, usually in pursuit of their prey.

Besides these general forms of distribution to suitable surroundings, we can observe a host of specialized adaptations, of a variety and interest sufficient to justify the immense work and the countless books and monographs that biologists have dedicated to them. We cannot give more than a glance at this subject.

We have already noticed that fishes living in holes are usually of an elongated shape. It is also well known that fishes living on the bottom have a tendency to assume a more or less flattened shape, or to have a short bulky body with large pectoral fins useful for short pounces (Bullheads). If we look closer we shall detect many small peculiarities that show how far this process of specialized adaptation may go.

We saw in the chapter on anatomy how important scales are to fishes and how sensitive many of them are to the loss of even a few scales. Aquarists are extremely careful in handling their fish; they know that Mackerel or Whiting invariably die if they have lost any scales, and that fungus attacks freshwater species in the same condition. But fish that rub against rocks, roots or snags, that hide under stones or in the sand, are protected against this danger. They either have no scales at all (Bullheads, both freshwater and marine, Shanny, Suckers, Conger, Turbot) or very small and firmly fixed scales (Sand-eels, Weevers), or a tough skin where the friction is greatest; the skin of the Common Eel (that is supplemented with slime and small scales) and that on the white side of the Sole are so tough that they are used as leather substitutes.

A flattened shape is most useful to bottom-haunting fishes, and we begin to notice it in that bane of sea anglers and first-year medical students, the Rough Hound, a small spotted dogfish common on our shores; its belly is flattened and its pectoral fins very broad. A step forward and we have the Monkfish or

Angelfish, intermediate in shape between Sharks and Rays. When this form of flattening and spreading has reached its maximum development, we have the Skates and Rays, with a small "squashed" body and immense fins that deserve the name of "wings" given to them by fishermen.

The other kind of flattening is very different. With the Rays the body is compressed between the back and the belly, while Plaice, Sole, Turbot, etc., are compressed on their sides, between right and left. Therefore the first group swims in the normal position of most fishes, while the second really swims sideways. All the species of this Order (*Heterosomata*), which includes all the true Flatfishes, start their life as normally shaped larval fishes, with a slim body and an eye on each side of the head. Soon, however, the tiny fish begins to go to the bottom, and to lie and swim on one side; one of the eyes manages, by passing either round the edge of the head or through it (this has not yet been proved with certainty), to join the other on one side of the body. The blind side remains white or light-coloured, while the other is turned uppermost and becomes dark. Some Flatfishes (Turbot, Brill, Megrim, Topknots) have their eyes on the left side, but in the majority of cases this is the blind side; freak individuals may not follow this rule, and it is not unusual to find Flounders with eyes on their left side.

We have already seen that oceanic fishes (Tunny, Bonito, Swordfish) have either perfectly streamlined bodies for rapid and constant swimming, or bulky and stocky build if they float more or less passively (Globefish, Sunfish). Some species have even managed to soar into the air to escape faster or more powerful enemies. On the other hand, fishes that remain on the bottom without giving evidence of much activity (Angler) have developed an external shape with appendages and frills that make them appear like a cluster of seaweed and marine growths, supplemented by a huge mouth constructed rather like an eel-basket or hoop-net, which victims can enter easily but where hinged teeth will prevent their getting out. This last adaptation is obviously an effective one, because we find it often among abyssal fishes. We have already seen that most of those ludicrous and nightmarish inhabitants of the dark depths of the oceans have an enormous mouth and stomach to accommodate very large though rare mouthfuls. Anglers of different species are to be found there, all having in common an exaggerated mouth and odd appendages. A group of deep-sea Anglers has also solved in a peculiar way the problem of making sure of a mate (as rare as food) without going to the trouble of seeking for one. In this type the female is many times larger than the male, which, after finding a spouse, gets a firm hold of her skin in such a way that his mouth fuses with her inner skin, and he is fed by her bloodstream; thus the tiny male remains fixed to his mate for life, living as a complete parasite.

Abyssal fishes live in surroundings where light cannot penetrate. They have solved the problem of living in perpetual darkness by adopting two diametrically opposed solutions: some of them have exceptionally large eyes and maybe luminous organs, while others are entirely blind and get their food by smell or feel. This course has also been followed by those few species that have invaded subterranean waters. Eyes were of no use to them and became atrophied, just as in our days we have seen men lose their power of reasoning in the unfavourable surroundings of tyranny.

FRESH OR SALT WATER. An adaptation of particular importance is that to fresh or salt water. Most people will never have thought about it, or maybe they have vaguely wondered why some fish live only in the sea and others only in fresh water. The point is rather puzzling, and unfortunately the explanation presupposes a certain knowledge of complicated physico-chemical laws (osmotic pressure and ionic dissociation) that would be entirely out of place in this book. The problem is very complex and difficult, and has not yet been thoroughly studied and solved. Still, it is so interesting and so little known to the public that it deserves an attempt at simple exposition.

If a bag of parchment paper is filled with a weak solution of sugar in water and is then kept for some time in a bowl of water made pink with a little red ink, the colourless sugar solution will acquire a pink tinge because water seeps through the parchment. Now reverse the experiment: colour pink the dilute sugar solution in the parchment bag, and dip it into colourless water—the inked liquid inside the bag will not colour the water outside. (Brother Physicist, we may neglect here the fact that parchment paper lets out a little sugar; we cannot all have $Cu_2Fe(CN)_6$ diaphragms.) This experiment will show that water seeps through what is called a "semi-permeable membrane," going from the weaker solution to the stronger, *but not vice versa*. If the stronger solution is put into a glass tube closed at the bottom by parchment paper or something of the kind, and dipped into water so that the liquid inside the tube is at the same level as the water outside, you will notice after some time that the level has changed and the solution inside the tube has risen a bit higher than the water outside. This second experiment shows that the seeping process (osmosis) is accompanied by a certain amount of force, sufficient to push up the level of the liquid.

Let us go back to our fish. Blood is a watery liquid, containing various salts in a weak solution, and sometimes special pigments that increase the capacity for oxygen absorption. Common worms have haemoglobin (an iron compound) dissolved in the blood, while vertebrates (including fish) have this compound in microscopic red corpuscles. Considered as a solution, the blood of fishes is stronger than fresh water and weaker than salt water; in neither medium is the fish's blood of the same concentration as the surrounding water.

The skin of fishes (excepting, as usual, Sharks and Rays) is protected, as we have already seen, by scales and slime. These two defences help considerably towards making a fish almost waterproof, and its skin, when undamaged, is not a "semi-permeable membrane." Nor is our own skin, and when we take a bath in fresh water we do not swell with water seeping into us. Only by the mouth and nose can we take in water; only through the gills can a fish. But the frilly nature of the gills gives a very large surface, which is always soaked in water for respiration. Therefore in freshwater fish water enters in large quantities through the gills to dilute the blood solution, while instead in a sea fish the weaker blood solution seeps out into the salt water. If there were no mechanisms of compensation, a freshwater fish would burst and a sea fish would dry up.

To adjust their physiological balance, freshwater fish cope with the excessive entry of water into their blood by *not drinking* and by excreting a very large quantity of dilute urine. Thus well-developed kidneys working at a very high rate eliminate the excess of water absorbed by the gills. (N.B.—The stomach of predaceous freshwater fishes has occasionally been found full of water.)

Sea fishes manage by following a completely different method. They *drink* a lot of water to make up for what they lose through the gills, and pass a small quantity of concentrated urine, excreting (as seems proved) salt in addition by means of special cells in the gills.

Sharks and Rays (Selachians) have a different system. Their blood contains a remarkably high quantity of urea, which gives it an osmotic pressure higher than that of sea water. In consequence they act like freshwater fishes; that is, they do not drink water and do excrete a large volume of dilute urine. It is worth pointing out that urea is a poisonous residue of the breaking-down of nitrogen-containing foods, and that in the majority of animals one of the most important functions of the kidneys is the complete elimination of urea; the Selachians instead do not suffer in the least from this compound.

There are fishes (such as the Sticklebacks, Trout, Eel, Salmon, Bass, Shads, etc.) that can live either in fresh or salt water. These species have kidneys capable of passing a large quantity of dilute urine, if necessary, and in fresh water they do not drink. The Eel is greatly protected by its thick slime. If the slime is removed

by continuous cleaning and the fish placed again in water, the lack
of protection will soon make itself manifest, in spite of the well-
known thickness and toughness of the Eel's skin, and the fish will
show clear signs of distress, until it manages to secrete some more
slime.

The rough handling of a fish with dry hands will remove slime
and scales, and not only make it liable to fungus infection but
will harm the delicately compensated system of water regulation.
So, once again, handle gently, with wet hands, and if possible
without removing it from the water, the fish you have caught
and that you intend setting free, at once or later on.

9

COLOUR AND COLORATION

COLORATION is a special biological term expressing the combination of colour with pattern; the colour of a tiger is yellow, white and black, which combined with the striped pattern makes its "coloration."

These two items enter so much into the mechanism of adaptation to surroundings that I have considered them worthy of a short chapter to themselves.

The silvery or white colour that is so prominent on the sides and under-parts of most fishes is due to the storing of a "refuse" or excretory substance called *guanin*, which is in the form of microscopical crystals. Another substance is black (*melanin*), and is the commonest insoluble colour or *pigment* found in animals, from the retina at the back of your eye to the "ink" of the squid. There are also two other important pigments, one reddish (carotene) and one yellow (xanthophyll).

It may seem that I have forgotten the beautiful shades of blue and green that you have seen on Mackerel, Herring, Roach and Bleak. They are due not to pigments but to the texture of the surface of the skin, and for this reason they are classified as "structural coloration." The same happens with many birds and insects, for similar reasons. In these cases there is a transparent layer over a dark pigment (usually melanin) acting rather like a mirror. There may be ripple marks on the scales due to growth, giving an irregular surface and thickness to the transparent layer of the scales. As a result, light is reflected at different angles, giving beautiful plays of colour and brilliant iridescent hues.

The coloured pigments are contained in small cells branching out in different directions; the pigment is in the form of a tiny speck in the centre of the cell, but, following impulses transmitted by the nervous system, it may spread more or less throughout the cell. Thus the different shades may vary in conspicuousness within a very wide range. The colour change may be almost instantaneous in some species, such as the Siamese Fighting Fish or the homely Bullhead; or it may take a fairly long time, maybe a few days (Rays). In most cases it is a question of a few hours.

Coloration and changes of colour may aim at concealment or display. The first is certainly the commonest and most important.

The fish world is a hungry one, and it is of the greatest help to be inconspicuous, either for defence or offence. One of the simplest and most effective forms of concealment is represented by counter-shading, when the intensity of the colours balances the intensity of the illumination; the more intense the light falling on a zone of the body, the darker it is coloured. As a result, a strong light is absorbed by the dark colours, while weak light is reflected by the white or pale zones of the body, making the animal inconspicuous. It is the arrangement that you may observe in a sparrow, a rabbit, a frog, or a Roach. In the Natural History Museum at South Kensington you can see an instructive model showing two bird-shaped dummies that can be rotated on a rod against a neutral background; the light comes from above, and you can notice at once how effective counter-shading can be in making an animal, even at a short distance, almost invisible.

Fishes enjoy an additional advantage from this device, because their dark backs are seen against the dark background of the bottom or of deep water, while their light-coloured bellies seen from below would tend to merge with the clear "window" of the sky appearing above them in the water. They would be less visible to birds or other fish from above or from preying animals rising from the bottom.

Countershading pure and simple is the only method of concealment of many species of fish, for instance Herring, Whiting, Carp, Chub, Bleak, Bream. Others add *disruptive coloration* to countershading, that is, a pattern of stripes, patches, blotches, spots or mottlings that merge with their surroundings (Plate 1). When you look at a handsome Perch with dark stripes descending from a deep olive back to a white belly, and bright crimson fins, you may think that such a gaudily marked creature would be easily seen; but if you try, even in favourable light, to see Perch against the weeds they haunt, you will soon discover that those stripes break the outline of the fish in such a way as to make it almost invisible in its surroundings. Fish living on a pebbly or gravelly bottom will melt into it if they are mottled or spotted like a Minnow, a Trout, a Gudgeon, a Plaice (Plate 2) or a Cod. Fish living on coral reefs have often the most vivid coloration imaginable: bold patterns and brilliant colours that have attracted painters even under the sea to paint these living jewels; but their surroundings are so brightly coloured that the fish become inconspicuous.

On special occasions or in particular cases fish may instead display their colours. The commonest instance is afforded by the *nuptial* coloration in the spawning season of such fish as, for instance, the male Minnow or the Stickleback of our streams, which assume bright red shades on their lower parts. During this season, the males of the whole Carp family have small white warts on their heads.

Wrasses, Dragonets, the beautiful tropical little fishes of the Cyprinodont group and the Stickleback are some of the best-known examples of bright colours displayed in courtship, and there is evidence that in some cases the females prefer the most gaudily coloured males, even among fishes.

A display of colours may also be due to anger, fear or hunger, that is, to emotions by which even fishes feel stirred. The Bull-head of our rills changes colour very quickly under the influence of these emotions; the Perch becomes lighter in colour when in "fighting attitude"; the Siamese Fighting Fish displays in combat a wide range of colours; the curiously shaped John Dory, when slowly stalking a small fish, shows its excitement by rapidly intensifying and fading its colours. Quite nice theories have been evolved to explain that fish and other creatures display these changes of colour in order to terrify their opponents or victims, or to assume a different appearance which presumably might help them to pass themselves off as something or somebody else. I have been unable to explain on the basis of these theories such commonplace phenomena as the paling of a frightened man or the blushing of an embarrassed youth. I am not disputing that some forms of coloration in animals may serve to intimidate aggressors (such as are found in wasps, cobras or skunks, to give a few known examples), nor that some forms of mimicry or imitation of dangerous animals (flies resembling wasps) may be justified. I merely wish to warn my readers against accepting too readily any attractive and all-explaining theory, or wanting to find some compulsory explanation for everything. In the field of animal coloration the temptation is very great; often the solution is obvious, sometimes it seems obvious; there is a tendency to accept as reasonable the idea that an animal adopts a certain appearance of its own volition (Lamarckism with a vengeance), out of mature reflection; if anybody suggested that you chose black hair or blond (on second thoughts I think I'll say black eyes or blue) of your own will, you will find the idea absurd. Equally absurd would be the suggestion that a Garfish had decided to have green bones for some wonderful reason.

Within a certain range the changes in colour depend on the reactions of the nervous system of fishes, and the general tendency is to approach as much as possible the colour and texture of the surroundings. A Tench from black mud may be nearly black, one from a light-coloured bottom may be greeny-yellow. Any angler can tell you that fish from neighbouring rivers or ponds, or from different stretches of the same river, may vary considerably in colour. Trout adopt so many varieties of coloured spots upon a background equally varied in colour, that from a single species the naturalist of sixty years ago deduced an entire range.

If you are fishing off a rocky coast, like Cornwall, you might come across a shoal of Wrasse, and capture a dozen or more, all resplendent in beautiful colours. On examining them closely, you may find that while the general pattern does not change much, there are perhaps no two fishes exactly the same. The Trunk-fishes of the Australian Great Barrier Reef are strange-looking creatures with dazzling colours and odd patterns, so varied that it is difficult to find two identical specimens. The Groupers (near relatives of our Wrasses) of Bermuda seem to make a sport of these changes of colour, and to assume any shade from uniformly dark to uniformly light, with a wealth of coloured bands or markings. If these fishes change their liveries for display, Flatfish change theirs for concealment and adapt their appearance to the sea floor to an amazing degree. Experiments carried out in the famous Naples Aquarium proved that a Mediterranean Flounder not only imitated perfectly the sandy, gravelly or shingly bottom, but could manage creditable imitations of artificial backgrounds of chessboard squares and black and white round spots.

These changes are carried out by nervous impulses given to the colour cells: the pigment spreads more or less throughout the surface of the cell, instead of remaining a small dot at its centre. The fish that adapts itself to the general colour and pattern of its surroundings does so through impulses received through its eyes. A Flounder placed with its head on a background of a certain shade assumed that shade for the whole of its body, although most of it was resting on a different background. Trout anglers will tell you that particularly dark Trout are blind and hunt only by smell; therefore, it is useless to try to cast a fly over them. On the contrary, fish living in dark caves are usually white or pink and their skin is without pigment; in a perpetually black world, there is no need for colours.

There are albino fishes, and others without melanin or certain pigments. The golden varieties of Carp, Tench, Orfe, etc., are due to this fact, as well as the uniformly silvery specimens of Goldfish.

NOTICE. From what we have seen we can conclude that *colours alone* are not a good guide in identifying a fish. It is for this reason that I have stressed the fixed characteristics of the different species; that is, anatomical peculiarities such as the number of scales and fin rays, position of fins and teeth, and proportional lengths of different parts of the body. *Only such characteristics are a safe guide towards identification.*

10

FEEDING

Third Fisherman : Master, I marvel how the
fishes live in the sea.
First Fisherman : Why, as men do a-land, the
great ones eat up the little ones.

(*Pericles*, II.)

ONLY those who indulge in widely advertised digestive remedies
can eat anything they want: others must eat what they can bite,
chew and digest, and the choice of food is severely restricted by
anatomical peculiarities. An ox with flat wide grinders, a special
stomach and a long intestine can live on grass, while a cat with
small sharp teeth and a short intestine must subsist on an easily
digested food, meat. The same rule applies to fishes. Every
imaginable vegetable or animal diet has been taken up by fishes
within the limits set by their surroundings and their anatomy.

Let us begin with the most widely accepted diet, other animals.
The majority of fishes are carnivorous with, as a rule, large mouths,
plenty of teeth (though the huge carnivorous Swordfish is toothless) and a short intestine. The gastric juice is very powerful,
and quickly dissolves the food, which is absorbed by the intestine.
The kind of animal food chosen and eaten depends on the size of
the eater and on its individual peculiarities of mouth. A small
fish, or one with a small mouth, is obviously obliged to restrict
itself to small prey; the tiny tube mouth of the Pipe-fishes enables
them to swallow very small shrimp-like creatures and similar
food. The sucker-like mouth of the Lampreys and Hagfishes has
no jaws, and the toothed tongue works like a rasp, scraping shreds
of flesh from the victims, that in this case are often much larger
than the attacker, so that one might call this class of fishes para-
sitical. Carnivorous fishes with a large mouth and pointed teeth
as a rule swallow their prey without cutting it or breaking it, and
in such cases the normal food is smaller fishes, crustaceans, worms,
insects or swimming molluscs. Other carnivorous species feed

on large crustaceans, sea-urchins, bivalve or univalve shell-fish; it is obviously necessary to chew or crush such food, and in order to do so the jaws are armed with powerful cutting and grinding teeth, such as would be required to crush lobsters, clams, cockles or whelks. In some cases there may be additional crushing teeth in the throat (pharyngeal teeth, such as are found in the Plaice or the Wrasses). Some species of Wrasses or Porcupine-fishes browse on corals, and are supplied with chisel-like cutting teeth on the edge of their mouths. Many Sharks and some Bony Fishes have rows of sharp, pointed teeth, arranged like the blades of scissors, enabling them to cut off lumps of flesh from their prey (Barracuda, Piranha of South American rivers). Lastly we may mention the abyssal fishes called Gulpers or Wide-mouths, that can chew more than they have bitten ; they are actually able to swallow fishes much larger than themselves because their jaws and stomachs are distensible like those of a snake, and, like a snake, they draw themselves over their prey, rather than draw it inside themselves, as do normal eaters.

Let us now turn to the plankton feeders, which eat the small forms of life, vegetable and animal, that float on the top of the sea. Countless millions of baby fishes live and grow on the surface, feeding on the minute diatoms and larval crustacea, echinoderms and worms of the upper layers; and here feed, on slightly larger plants and animals, immense shoals of Herrings, Sprats, Pilchards and the like, as well as the huge Whale Shark and Basking Shark, the two giants among fish. The gill-rakers of these plankton feeders are usually long, thin and closely spaced, so as to collect and sift the food in the water, which water passes through the gill-openings, leaving the food to be swallowed. The Herrings and their like are in turn eaten by pelagic fish, such as Tunnies, Swordfish and some Sharks.

The vegetarians and mud eaters are mostly found in fresh water. Their mouths are toothless or equipped only with weak teeth, their intestines long and coiled, their stomachs occasionally act as a gizzard, and they have often throat teeth to assist in breaking up the food. Our Cyprinids (Carp family) and Grey Mullets are among the best-known examples. They feed on water plants, shoots and seeds, on fine algal growths (such as the "silkweed" of weirs) or seaweeds (Parrot-fish, for example), with the addition, in our rivers, of food kindly supplied by anglers in the form of bait and ground-bait. In making this statement I am not aiming at a feeble joke, but stating a fact; a Lancashire Food Inspector has formally declared that before the war the eight or nine hundred competitors at the annual Wigan Angling Centre match used in two hours some 3,200 lb. of stale bread as ground-bait; and anyone who has seen the prodigal scattering of ground-bait at "Hempseed Corner" near Richmond will agree with me. Many vegetarian fishes are also mud eaters; they swallow mouthfuls of mud for the organic matter it contains, consisting of decaying vegetation and small creatures living on it. A few species subsist entirely on mud, and this rather unattractive diet occupies a large place in the feeding of such well-known fish as the Carp and the Tench.

All freshwater fishes, carnivorous or vegetarian (excepting perhaps a few plankton eaters, such as the Whitefish), partake at all or some periods of their lives of insects (both the perfect insect and the larval forms represented by grubs, maggots or nymphs developing in water), worms, crustacea and molluscs, as well as the eggs and fry of their own or other species; these last items being considered particularly attractive, even by such mild vegetarians as Roach or Carp. Indeed, the fish world represents the ideal development of the Big Business principle. Anyone *may* eat anyone else: the big fish may eat the little one, and the little one *may* eat the big one; if he *can* not, why, it is indeed his own funeral. Luckily the fish world is better arranged than the Big Business one; there we can see the survival of the fittest, which does not mean the survival of the biggest or most rapacious.

II

MIGRATIONS

WE may travel for pleasure, but fish travel only on business, vital business—the life of the individual or that of the species. All fishes travel in search of food or more suitable surroundings, and for breeding. But the vagaries of a Roach in a stretch of river or of a Carp in its pond are as commonplace as our daily trip to factory, office, shop or school. It is only the big journey that becomes important.

Some oceanic species are always travelling: they are the sea rovers, going after food anywhere, always, such as some Sharks, the Swordfish and some members of the Tunny or Mackerel tribe. They travel alone or in small groups, but other fish travel in shoals, sometimes of immense size. The migrations of these species are to a large extent controlled by temperature. This influence may be direct, such as when the warmth-loving Mackerel leave in winter the cold water near the shore to retire to deeper and more acceptable surroundings, returning to the shallows only when the spring and summer sunshine has warmed them again. The Pilchard or Sardine leaves the Spanish or Portuguese coasts only in summer, and does not go farther north than Cornwall. The influence may be indirect, as when the cold or changes in sea currents (failing to bring fresh supplies of "manurial" salts) affect the growth of the plankton or other food, and oblige fish, as they oblige birds, to migrate in search of it. To this we owe the Codlings that in winter attract anglers on the East Anglian beaches and the Channel piers. Warmth may have the effect of stopping migratory habits. The Char (*Salvelinus alpinus*) in Arctic waters goes to sea like a Sea Trout and enters rivers to spawn, but in warmer latitudes its sub-species inhabit fresh water only (British Isles, Alpine lakes). The Trout does the same, though at a different latitude; it becomes an exclusively freshwater species in the Mediterranean. The Stickleback is prevalently a marine species in Arctic waters; it lives both in sea and fresh water (going from one to the other without any difficulty) in our islands, but is restricted to fresh water in Mediterranean countries.

The Herring may be taken as a convenient example of a fish always on the move, either for food or for spawning purposes. The great fisheries of our Commercial Fish No. 1 catch the Herrings while they are on either kind of travel. The North Shields and the Shetland fisheries catch feeding Herrings, while the great East Anglian season in the autumn gets fish with a stomach shrunken through a prolonged fast. There are several "races" or immense shoals of Herrings with common peculiarities, habits, distribution, places and seasons of spawning, and a detailed study of them is still being made.

Spawning migrations are the most spectacular: the Salmon racing up their native river, or the Eels swarming down towards the depths of the Atlantic, have rightly attracted the attention of Man for centuries. An inadequate description of their migrations will be found in the chapters dedicated to these two species. Other fishes enter fresh water to spawn, and among our British species we may number the Lampreys, the Smelt and the Shads.

The Flounder leaves the estuaries and the shore to spawn in deeper water in the sea, and other Flatfish follow its example. The Anchovy travels a long way from its warm seas to spawn in the shallow waters round Holland. The Tunny leaves the Atlantic to go to well-known coasts in the Mediterranean, where important fisheries have existed for centuries on the same spots. When not on this spawning migration the Tunny is a wanderer, voyaging anywhere where it can find small fish to eat, and following equally the Herring shoals that appear off Scarborough or those off Nova Scotia, one side of the Atlantic being as good as the other if it offers food.

Lastly, I shall mention some peculiar causes of migrations or journeys. The Stickleback occasionally multiplies in enormous quantities, and huge shoals of this minute fish may be seen "making the water almost solid," as one witness described it. Exceptional migrations take place also among other species, probably for the same reason. Fish may migrate permanently to or from a district because of pollution, or changes in the salinity of the water, or the appearance or disappearance of food. Shoals of Herrings change their course if they come across patches of a minute plant, a diatom called Rhizosolenia, that, being long and sharp, apparently injures their gills.

12

THE IMPORTANCE OF FISH

FISH are supremely important to themselves, of course, just as we are to ourselves. They are also very important to us, and I wanted to give a convincing collection of statistical data, covering not only the fishing industry but also other industrial and commercial activities connected with fish, such as fish-curing and exporting, fishing-tackle production, fish by-products (oils, glue, manure, skins, etc.). Unfortunately the Board of Trade during the war forbade the publication of any recent statistical information. I could, of course, give some old figures taken from the *Encyclopaedia Britannica*, but such information could be easily got by any reader who wishes it. The only recent figures appear in the White Paper on the War Effort (November 1944), where it is stated that the landings of wet fish of British taking during 1938 amounted to 1,045,350 tons.

I shall have to content myself with giving a rather incongruous medley of scraps of information, all tending to prove that fish are important to mankind.

Let us begin with the most obvious point of view, that of food. Fish are an important item of diet, both for quantity and quality. The flesh of fish is tasty, easily digested and nutritious, with a high "calorie" or energy value. Herring, Salmon and Mackerel (in good condition, of course) are at least equal in food value to beef or mutton; the Eel is much superior, but "white" and most freshwater fish are inferior to meat.

It is difficult to calculate the amount and value of all fish captured in different countries. An American estimate, very much on the conservative side, values all catches at 800 million dollars a year, or £200 millions sterling; the British output was about one-tenth of that figure.

On the basis of other old statistics, the average annual British catch in the 1925–1929 period offers some interesting facts. The biggest catch was that of the Herring (almost 390,000 tons), bigger than those of the Cod (over 170,000 tons) and Haddock (over 150,000 tons) combined. The fishes next in importance are a long way behind; they were the Hake (over 44,000 tons), the Plaice (about 34,000 tons), the various Skates and Rays (28,000 tons) and the Whiting (less than 25,000 tons). The poor "General Public" would be rather surprised at knowing that they have eaten large quantities (almost 18,000 tons) of fish they have never heard mentioned, such as Wolf-fish or Megrim, not to mention over 7,000 tons of Dogfish; the Megrim went as Plaice or Lemon Sole; the Wolf-fish, with many other "unknowns," under the all-embracing title "rock salmon" (that includes sometimes even Dogfish). The only freshwater species of commercial importance are the Salmon (see page 114) and the Eel, imported from Holland in special boats; excluding the Salmon, the amount of freshwater fish marketed in Britain reaches a few hundred tons a year, mostly Eel, Trout and Carp.

Before the first World War enormous amounts of Herring were exported, mostly to Russia; the average yearly "cure" was about 2 million barrels.

In these days, when vitamins are considered a panacea, fish oils are likely to be valued only as sources of medicines, although they have been for many years much sought after in the manufacture of soft soaps and chamois leather, for the softening of hides, for steel tempering and, after hydrogenation, for the preparation of edible fats. These oils are extracted from the whole fish, when the fatty substances are diffused in the tissues (Herring, Menhaden), or from the liver, when the oil is stored in this organ (Cod family, Halibut, Sharks and Rays). It is from these that medicinal extracts are obtained, the vitamin concentration varying not only from species to species but also with the season and method of extraction. It has recently been found that the Stone Bass and other Sea Perches yield oils with a high vitamin content. Norway was the biggest European source of fish oils; she produced yearly about a million and a half gallons of cod-liver oil alone.

Isinglass is manufactured from the air-bladder of several fishes, the best and most used being made from the Sturgeon's. Other qualities are obtained from the air-bladders of members of the Cod family and other species. Fish-glue is made from the skins of several species of Cod, and when dissolved in acetic acid it yields adhesives of great power. Lower grades of glue are made from fish heads.

Fish scraps and unmarketable kinds are transformed into fish meal, an excellent additional protein food for poultry and other farm animals. Fertilizers, rich in nitrogen and phosphorus, are made from unwholesome fish, as well as from fish offal.

The economic importance of fish to the fish trades needs no comment, although one might easily overlook the industries that reap work and profit indirectly from those trades. Railways, packers, timber merchants, tinplate makers, coopers, box and case manufacturers, shipbuilders, net-yarn spinners, etc., share with the fisherman and the fishmonger the bounty from the sea. I wished to give some data about the fishing-tackle industry that has sent British goods of the highest quality to all corners of the earth; unfortunately war-time restrictions prevent me from doing so. I must not neglect, however, to pay my small tribute to an industry that engages not only about half of the firms of Redditch (the world centre of fishing-tackle making) and many others outside, but also very many home craftsmen of the highest skill. I owe to the courtesy of the Redditch U.D.C. the information that nine-tenths of the world production of fishing tackle comes from that town; other countries may perhaps dispute that figure, but no one could deny that British firms, some over a century old, manufacture goods that do honour to their country.

Fish-skins are a valuable source of special leathers, The most used are those from Sharks and Rays, the humble Dogfish included; if the little spiny placoid scales are left in the skin, we have the material known as shagreen; if the scales are larger, the hide may be used to sandpaper wood. During the last twenty years or so shark skins have acquired a greater commercial importance because means have been found to remove the scales and tan the hide in a very satisfactory manner. This kind of leather is tough and waterproof, and much valued for special purposes. Other fish skins have been tried, but generally speaking they lack toughness. During the war the Danes made ladies' shoes with the uppers of Sole skin; I doubt if this fashion will continue now that peace has returned. The rather beautiful ornamental leather called "sea-leopard" is obtained from the tough, scaleless skin of the Wolf-fish; this unfortunate giant Blenny has failed to get its name preserved in the trade: its flesh becomes "rock salmon," its skin "sea-leopard."

Having paid due homage to the serious, sound and (of course) supremely important trade interests connected with fishes, may I be allowed to break a lance in favour of one of the oldest occupations or sports, Angling? After all, angling matters a lot, or a little, to several hundred thousand people in the British Isles. The British Federation of Angers used to have about 120,000 members. This figure represents a very small portion of all the British anglers. The Clerks of two of the most important Fishery Boards have courteously given me the number of licences (Salmon excluded) taken out in their districts for 1938, the last peace year. In the Severn Fishery 85,040 were granted, and 87,127 in the Trent Fishery. If we consider that the Thames district requires no licences, that no licences are needed for sea fishing, and that only a small part of the angling fraternity joins clubs, I believe we could conservatively estimate the number of regular anglers at over 300,000. Add the occasional anglers who dangle a handline from a boat or a pier and the boys trying for minnows (and why should we not count them?), and the angling population will assume proportions large enough to be called "respectable." Anglers are many, then. Perhaps too many, according to their wives. Still I hope that many more will join the brotherhood of the Angle. By anglers I do not mean destroyers of fish, measuring their success by the number of creatures they kill. I remember a great angler saying that "there is more in fishing than catching fish." Of course there is, infinitely more. I could not do better than quote a few passages from Izaak Walton, the "Father of Anglers." This is what he says: "You have heard many grave, serious men, pity Anglers. . . . Men that are taken to the grave, because nature hath made them of a sour complexion; money-getting men, men who spend all their time, first in getting, and next in anxious care to keep it; men that are condemned to be rich, and then always busy and discontented; for these poor rich men, we Anglers pity them perfectly, and stand in no need to borrow their thoughts to think ourselves so happy. No, no, we enjoy a contentedness above the reach of such dispositions. . . . Most Anglers are quiet men, and followers of peace; men so simply wise, as not to sell their consciences to buy riches, and with them vexation and a fear to die. . . No life so happy and so pleasant as the life of a well-governed angler, for when the lawyer is swallowed up with business, or the statesman is preventing or contriving plots, then we sit on cowslip banks, hear the birds sing, and possess ourselves in as much quietness as those silent silver streams, which we now see glide so quietly by us. . . . God never did make a more calm, quiet, innocent recreation than Angling."

In these days, when existence becomes more and more communal and machine-made (even if the machines be human) and our amusements become more and more external, there are fewer chances than in Walton's time for that "contemplation" he prized so much, though the need is even greater. Brother Reader, try angling; you may catch very few fish, or none, but you will be perhaps richer in spirit than you were before. You cannot abide fishing? Choose bird-watching, studying pond-life, mountain climbing, any occupation you like and that *you* have to do, alone or with a very few friends. It is difficult to be alone to-day, but, as Samuel Johnson said, it is only in solitude that we have our dreams to ourselves. You will have a pastime in which you, and you alone, can supply the enjoyment: no professional specialist can give it to your eyes or ears. *You* will have to make efforts; your success will be due to your knowledge and skill, and your failure cannot be blamed on others. It will be always new, "for Angling may be said to be so like the Mathematicks that it can never be fully learned." While you are taking a recreation that depends on your own endeavour, in the best surroundings that God made, you are living *to-day*, instead of working, worrying or planning to live *some other time*, as most of us do most of our time. You will enter the Brotherhood of the Angle, and you will find true brothers everywhere and among everybody; there are no races or classes among fishermen: even the Important Man, if he is a true angler, will be your friend. You think I am talking a lot about my hobby, but if you become one of us you will find that it is not only a hobby: it is a philosophy of life, that may help you to find in yourself that happiness which, however hard to find there, cannot be found anywhere else.

13

FISH PRESERVATION

> "There are as good fish in the sea as ever came
> out of it."
> (*Old proverb, hotly denied by fishermen.*)

IF you read any old angling books or old statistics of sea fishing,
and compare the catches of those days, both in quantity and
quality, with the best of ours, you will be struck by the change.
An average catch of the past would be an abnormally good one
in our times. The ease with which Izaak Walton caught trout
in the Lea would make any modern angler's mouth water,
especially as Trout are rare in the lower Lea nowadays. In his
angling reminiscences Peard tells that in 1862 he made wonderful
catches of big Trout in several Irish loughs; his baskets for one day
would now be considered good enough for a month. Several
Commissions, enquiring into the troubles afflicting trawlermen
and long-liners, have come to the conclusion that North Sea
fishing has greatly deteriorated. With fishing in the sea, and
even more in fresh water, as with songs and modern youth,
things are never so good as they used to be.

Human-wise, we have blamed anything and everything for
this state of things but ourselves. Otters, eels, artificial fertilizers,
hempseed and God knows what bore the guilt for the shocking
diminution of freshwater fish. At sea the long-liners blame the
trawlers, the trawlermen blame the seine and trammel men, all
curse the something foreigners, with other culprits such as oil-
burning ships, invasions by Dogfish and supposed changes of
sea currents thrown in. The Trout addict says that if only Grayling
and coarse fish were exterminated the fishing would be marvel-
lous; the Grayling or "coarse" enthusiasts are sure that if Trout
were fewer things would improve, and just for once the pursuer
of Salmon will condescend to agree with that lowly crowd. If
anybody dares to point out that in the (really) good old days all

78

these fish managed to prosper side by side, in spite of a multitude of Eels, he becomes unpopular with all. At sea everything would be fine if only foreigners did not exist except as customers: in Ireland the villains are the French trawlers, in Iceland and Norway their place is taken by British ships, while British fishermen have the satisfaction of having a greater range of foreigners to curse. In the midst of this sulphureous atmosphere of reciprocal blame, matters go from bad to worse because the two real causes are neglected.

The trouble is due to *pollution* and *overfishing*. In fresh water the two causes are more or less evenly balanced; at sea overfishing on an almost total scale is practically the whole trouble.

Our lakes and rivers have been and continue to be poisoned by every kind of stuff that greedy, lazy, stingy or stupid people have thought fit to throw into them. The sewers of towns, the refuse of copper or lead works or of any factory with filth to get rid of, the "carbolic-y" washings off roads covered with cheap, impure tar by mean-minded road-building authorities, the rubbish tips of villages, all have contributed to sully the streams and destroy life in them. Garbage floats down to the sea until it meets the tides, which confine it within the estuary, drifting up and down and slowly putrefying; there this filth remains until corruption has dissolved it, making the water uninhabitable for any fish, because the process of decomposition takes the oxygen from the water and releases harmful gases such as sulphuretted hydrogen. The supply of sewage and garbage is unending, and permanently pollutes the water and air of some large estuaries, forming an impassable barrier to Salmon, Trout, Lampreys, Shad, Smelt, and thinning out even the elvers that should become Eels.

All animal and a good deal of plant life in a lake or stream may be destroyed by pollution in a few hours or days, but years may pass before those waters can be repopulated by fish. First plant life must be re-established from roots or new seeds; then small creatures, such as water-fleas, appear, and the larvae of flying insects, followed slowly by crustacea (freshwater shrimps and crayfish) and by a few fish emigrating from other waters; these will multiply at every spawning season, but their offspring can reproduce only when they have reached maturity, after three or four years. If the water is not connected with other streams or ponds, artificial restocking with fish, shrimps, etc., is the only cure. If pollution continues, not only is there no animal life, but plants, too, may be killed off altogether and the stretch of water turned into a stinking, useless ditch; badly polluted streams are devoid even of birds.

The remedy lies in the hands of all of us. There are societies nobly struggling against this evil, but they have never received sufficient support from the public. I cannot give much space to this subject, and I must hurry on with my suggestion. First of all, you, reader, stop using a stream for a garbage dump, whether you live by one or go to one for a picnic. Then, as a voter, taxpayer, ratepayer or citizen, insist that your town, borough or village uses its sewage in a clean, sensible and profitable way, instead of pouring it into the nearest brook. There are a few enlightened towns with modern sewage plants, where this obnoxious refuse is properly fermented and treated, with the result that instead of being a nuisance it becomes a source of first-class fuel (it yields large quantities of methane or marsh gas, that would supplement the local gas output or could be used industrially) and of an excellent natural fertilizer, rich in nitrogen and phosphorus, odourless and cheap—so cheap that before the war large quantities of this "dry sludge" were exported to France and Belgium, where many people had the sense to buy it. Lastly, in your own interest, see that no smart manufacturer saves a packet at the expense of your pocket. If you don't, you may have the gratification of hearing that the manager, or the biggest shareholder, has bought a salmon river in Scotland for his own exclusive delectation, at the cost of the relaxation you and your fellow citizens used to get on your home river. If you oppose those arrangements you will be accused of obstructing progress, sapping individual initiative, interfering with business and what not;

you will be reminded of the two slogans on which the "wonderful" prosperity of last century was founded: *laisser faire—laisser passer*. You might answer with Sismondi's century-old reply: "You really mean *laisser faire la misère—laisser passer la mort*"; you may add that far from interfering with other people's initiative and individuality you wish to keep some for yourself, and that you do not feel like letting monopolists and officials (in firms as well as in Unions or public offices) arrange your life according to their wishes (or advantages); lastly, that business and progress that benefit some people or groups at the expense of the community are bad business and no progress. As sermons are more effective if supported by the awful example of what befell another sinner, I shall tell what happened in Italy in 1928, under the rule of that (then) much-praised system of tyranny which, by forcibly depriving Italians of their individuality, made at their expense the fortune of many unscrupulous businessmen and fascist officials. The lovely lake of Orta, near Lake Maggiore, had a great wealth of water life: it was teeming with many species of fish (some found only there) and crustacea. A large artificial-silk factory was opened near by, and the copper and ammonia refuse of the cuprammonium process was poured into the lake. All aquatic life in the lake and its emissary was killed; the fishermen were ruined (they were small people, so they did not matter), the stench of rotting fish drove visitors from hotels and homes, and small businesses catering for the fishermen were also ruined. And do not think these things happen only among foreigners. If you prefer an example nearer home, you ought to read, for instance, the excellent paper on the ecology of the Trent, written by an expert, Major Inglis Spicer, Clerk and Biologist to the Trent Fishery Board. He has kindly allowed me to quote a few extracts. He remarks that the subsistence of fish in rivers is an index of the standard of purity essential to such waters if they are to serve industrial, agricultural and domestic purposes. He adds: "Growing congestion in industrial communities sent the workers looking for health-giving recreation for themselves and their families, and a tremendous coarse-fishing angling fraternity has made a place for itself in the national life of the country. One in ten of the insured workers in the Trent Fishery District are licensed anglers following a recreation with apparent national advantages, quite apart from the circulation in this district alone of about £1,500,000 per annum." Having established these points, the author gives numerous instances of the havoc played by pollution in the Trent river system, where "there are over one hundred out of a total of five hundred and fifty miles of flowing water where neither animal nor plant life can subsist, and in little more than half of the total mileage can fish live with safety." In consequence, not only professional and amateur fishing have grievously suffered, but "industrialists looking for expansion are finding that polluted water-courses prohibit development of many otherwise desirable sites." In conclusion I will quote one last passage: "It will be seen therefore that industrial urban expansions have set their own limits by short-sightedness, permitted by absence of national policy. The experience of the Trent Fishery Board in its work since 1923 has clearly shown that there are few, if any, industries in which provision for the reasonable purification of their waste waters would be impracticable or even a serious charge on the industry. Any urban community should be able to provide for the adequate treatment of its waste waters on an annual expenditure of half a crown a head of its population out of the normal revenue of £8 per head from rates for such a community."

The other cause of destruction, overfishing, is due to you, amateur angler and professional fisherman, and the remedy is also in your hands. The remedy for overfishing is staggeringly obvious: fish less. Or, at least, kill less fish. You cannot kill your fish and catch it. The problem of overfishing at sea and the best remedies have been most ably dealt with by Michael Graham in his *Fish Gate*, and you can hardly do better than read that book, which advocates a sensible international agreement among fishermen to regulate the fishing industry; to "regulate" doesn't mean only to restrict output and raise prices; it means to put some rule in place of chaos. I shall content myself with remarking that at sea the destruction of an incredible amount of spawning and immature fish goes on undisturbed. A few years ago the Ministry of Agriculture and Fisheries issued a regulation forbidding the "capture" of Flatfish under 9 in. in length, and of small Hake and Whiting. To the protests of fishermen, who pointed out that it is a bit difficult to avoid catching fish in a trawl at the bottom of the sea, the Ministry's officials (possibly thinking in terms of fresh-water angling) replied allowing very kindly the capture of small fish, provided they were thrown back into the sea; the good bureaucrats had never seen, obviously, the cod-end of a trawl, and did not know that badly mauled young fish could not survive, even if the busy trawlermen (and how busy they are, poor devils!) could pick out every single specimen and drop it gently into the sea, keeping the gulls away in the meantime. In the face of this absurdity that other one of lumping the dwarf Dab together with the giant Halibut becomes almost insignificant. It would be better to try to find some way of checking the wholesale slaughter of baby Flatfish caused by the shrimp industry, or the destruction of spawning fish. Dr. Travis Jenkins mentions, for instance, that two of the three spawning grounds of the Sole in the Irish Sea have been heavily overfished, and that the third is suffering the same fate.

In fresh water the overfishing problem could be easily solved by anglers, if they so wished. It depends entirely on their common sense and sportsmanship. There are closed seasons and minimum legal sizes for freshwater fish; in some districts there are even maximum numbers allowed for certain species. These are excellent arrangements, but they are not enough. It is all very well to spare immature fish, but if we kill all the adult ones they will not be able to multiply, and soon there won't be any left for the angler. If we spared all lambs and killed all sheep, very soon there would not be any mutton. If you are so lucky or skilful as to catch twenty pounds of Roach, you are certainly not going to eat, stuff, or sell the lot; not even if you catch five pounds. Have you got a big specimen? Display it in a glass case, by all means; after all, you won't catch many whoppers. Do you want to eat a Perch or two? Certainly, they are a tasty dish. And what about the rest, the smaller fish you could not help catching? Put them in a keep net, if you like, till the end of the day, and then return them *gently* to liberty. They will grow and multiply, providing you and your brother anglers with more and better sport. I can understand (though I loathe it) that a child, with the ignorant and callous cruelty of youth, could kill for nothing and waste that irreplaceable thing that is life. But I cannot understand grown-up men (unless they are brutish or selfish) indulging in so stupid and barbarous an action.

The preservation of our freshwater fish is important from other points of view than that of angling. Fish have their place in the balance of nature, and their destruction upsets that balance. One of the causes for the rapid and strange decline of the ancient Greek civilization was, according to some people, the wholesale destruction of freshwater fish. For with their reduction, it is contended, the mosquito larvae, no longer being kept down by fish, developed into flying insects on a vast scale, and in so doing spread malaria at a rate that made the Macedonian conquest possible where the Persian hordes had failed. This explanation is perhaps too simple to be wholly satisfactory, but it cannot be denied that a little Cyprinodont (the "Millions" fish) has kept Barbados free from yellow fever, and that the introduction of this or similar species in mosquito-infested districts has helped in combating both malaria and yellow fever.

A last word. Please do not airily imagine that artificial hatching, rearing and restocking could at any time put things magically right. Freshwater and anadromous species may draw considerable benefit from these operations, although they are necessarily expensive and often heartbreakingly disappointing. But when we pass to sea fish it is quite another story. Fulton and Jenkins, with the authority that their years of painstaking work deserves, have expressed serious doubts as to the results of marine hatching and stocking experiments. The only people who have no doubts are those who want to go on fishing without restraint, and since *is dixit cui prodest*, we are justified in being inclined to accept the opinion of unbiased scientists rather than that of those engaged in commercial concerns.

14

FISH COOKING

Hamlet : . . . You are a fishmonger.
Polonius : Not I, my lord.
Hamlet : Then I would you were so honest a man.
(*Hamlet*, II, 2.)

As a general rule, fish (and not fish alone) is badly cooked in England; my kin across the Irish Sea are even worse offenders. Apart from a few oases the only places where fish is cooked in an appetizing way are the highest and lowest (I mean the costliest and the cheapest) establishments: the hotel or restaurant with a grand French or Italian chef, and the humble fish-and-chip shop.

The fundamental mistakes are: prejudice against any unfamiliar fish—frying oily fish and boiling white fish—boiling fish instead of steaming or poaching it—total ignorance about cooking fish in any way that is not frying or boiling.

The British housewife knows only a few kinds of fish: herrings, sprats, cod, plaice, hake, mackerel, skate, sole and very few more, varying from place to place. Offer her bass, mullets or John Dory and she will turn her nose away in disgust; even when these fish are sold cheaper than stale cod, as I saw a few days before writing these lines. She wants to buy the kind she knows, and only those, irrespective of their being in season or not. She considers the delicious and nourishing herring a low, proletarian fish, and believes skate or cod to be superior food. She may point out, acridly, that herrings "stink the house" ; sure they do, because housewives have never insisted on having at least a galvanized iron chimney over their fires, so that the cookery fumes could be conveyed outside, as can be found in restaurants and fish shops. Ask your fishmonger's advice: he will be glad, even grateful, to help you with his counsel. If he tells you that the weird-looking John Dory is as good as sole or turbot, he is stating a true fact. Be ready to buy gurnard and sea-bream, grey mullet and Norway haddock on his advice, rather than stale and watery whiting or haddock. It will not be necessary then to invent names in order to persuade the public to buy unfamiliar fish, and rock salmon or flake will become honest wolf-fish, coalfish, dogfish or tope.

"White" fish, such as the members of the Cod and Plaice families, have their fat stored in their livers, instead of its being diffused in the flesh (Salmon and Herring families). They ought to be fried, preferably in batter, as the fish shop does. If you boil them, you must expect them to taste like wet flannel. This remark applies also to most freshwater fishes.

Please, *do not boil* fish, especially freshwater kinds. Put the fish in salted water or (even better) fish stock, just enough to cover it. Bring gently to the boil, and then let it simmer in the slowest possible way. Then the flesh will remain intact, instead of breaking up and letting the flavour ooze out into the water. White and freshwater fish up to a couple of pounds may take about 10 minutes cooking (at boiling-point), while fish up to four pounds require from 15 to 20. Some fish with compact flesh (such as trout, carp or gurnard) may take twice as long.

This book deals mostly with freshwater fish, among which are some species (Salmon family) that remain good in spite of bad cooking, and others that are uneatable unless properly cooked. Sea fish are an easier proposition, but many of them, especially the "white" kind, are vastly improved if cooked according to the recipes for "coarse" freshwater fish.

I come now to the recipes.

Fish Stock. Fish are much improved if steamed in fish stock instead of plain water. Put in slightly salted cold water the bones, heads and trimmings of fish, adding a little sliced onion, parsley or celery leaves, and a few peppercorns; bring to the boil, let it simmer for half an hour; when almost cold strain and add a little white wine or vinegar.

This stock, with suitable additions, is excellent for preparing fish sauces, especially after fish has been steamed in it. Mix a little cornflour with the cold stock, and put it on the fire, adding a piece of butter; heat gently, stirring the whole time, until it thickens. Then add a little more butter, and stir it into the mixture until cooked. You may add anchovy or bloater paste, mashed boiled shrimps, capers or chopped parsley with the last of the butter.

Baked "Coarse" or White Fish. Fillet, wash and dry the fish, that may be any "coarse" (perch, roach, bream, etc.) or "white" (cod, whiting, haddock, etc.) fish. Melt a little margarine in an oven dish, and place the fillets in it, after spreading them with anchovy or bloater paste. Cover the fish with a layer of breadcrumbs mixed with grated cheese. Bake in a hot oven for about half an hour or a little more, according to the thickness of the fillets. Serve with parsley or caper sauce.

Savoury Meunière. A capital recipe for chub, roach and other doubtful favourites is due to Major Cornwallis-West, who kindly allows me to publish it. Parboil (time according to size of fish), remove from utensil, then skin, split down back and lift out the bones; then fillet and fry in breadcrumbs with chopped onions or chives and sage or other herbs according to taste. Add a teaspoonful of Worcester or other savoury sauce to the margarine when frying. Serve with contents of frying-pan as a sauce.

Fried Fish à la Meunière. The simplest way of frying fish and one of the best. Small fish (or flatfish) may be used whole; larger ones must be cut into fillets or slices. Season the fish with salt and pepper, flour it and fry it in *very hot* shallow butter until golden. Remove it, but keep it warm; sprinkle it with finely chopped parsley and a little lemon-juice. Melt a little more butter in the pan, fry it till pale brown, pour it on the fish and serve immediately.

Paper-bag Cooking. Many years ago there was a craze for paper-bag baking, and it is still a method to be recommended for fish. If the fish is small (not more than a quarter of a pound), it may be used whole; large fish must be cut into slices about one inch thick. Smear the fish with thick sauce, or with oil or butter, add a squeeze of lemon, wrap up each piece in well-greased paper, and twist the end of this packet. Bake in a moderate oven for 20 to 30 minutes.

Stewed Fish. It is a pity that no more use is made of stewing, as many fish of no great flavour are vastly improved by such a treatment. A good recipe will be found on page 152; it is particularly good for "coarse" fish. A simpler recipe is the following one.

Clean and scale the fish and lay it on the bottom of a low saucepan or casserole, and cover it with vegetable, meat or fish stock, to which you have added wine to taste, or tomato juice, or a little vinegar. Season, add finely chopped onion and a pinch of herbs, and boil *gently* for 20 to 30 minutes. When the fish is cooked, remove it from the saucepan, add to the gravy a little cornflour to thicken it and a generous spoonful of chopped parsley; boil for a few minutes and pour it over the fish. Serve hot.

Grilled Fish. Fish must be grilled slowly and well basted. Unless the fish are very small, it is well to cut a few gashes on their sides. Serve with a good sauce.

To Remove Muddy Tang. The fish of the Carp family are very often made uneatable by a muddy flavour. This may be removed to a great extent if you clean the fish as soon as possible, and rub plenty of salt well into it, not forgetting the mouth, throat and gills; leave overnight or longer, then rinse thoroughly; lastly rub some vinegar inside.

To Remove Flesh from Bones. The fish of the Herring and Carp families are notoriously plagued with a multitude of fine bones. You will fare better if you follow these instructions.

If you eat the skin, start splitting the fish into two fillets *from the back*, not the belly. Insert your knife along the dorsal fin from head to tail, edging the blade inside along the backbone and gently lifting the flesh from the "ribs"; if you carry out the job properly, very few bones will remain inside the fillets. If you do not eat the skin, remove it first. Along the middle of both sides of the fish you will see a line, separating the lower from the upper portion of flesh; cut in from the back of the fish or from the middle line, lifting or pushing aside the flesh. In either case, once you have managed one side, turn the fish on the other and start afresh. If you cut your fish from the belly upwards, you will get most of the bones off the skeleton, and into your mouth.

Try these two methods on your herrings, and if it encourages you to eat a few more of them, we shall both have given some help to the drifter fishermen.

15

AN AQUARIUM AT HOME

EVERY day large numbers of visitors to the London Zoo pay an extra 6d. to see the aquarium, and do not regret the expense. Many, indeed, seized with an immediate urge to keep fishes for themselves, call in at Woolworth's on the way home, or take a trip to the local pet store, to buy a few goldfish with which they overcrowd a small glass bowl. The inevitable sequel is sad and salutary. The unfortunate fishes, congested, unable to breathe, feed or move with any comfort, die off one by one, and the disappointed aquarist gives up the job in disgust, blaming everybody but himself for the failure.

It is beyond the scope of this book to give specialized instructions for the successful management of an aquarium. If I can convince you that the keeping of fishes at home requires neither deep learning nor hard labour, this chapter will have served its purpose. What is necessary, however, is a strict attention to a few elementary rules, which are (one would think) obvious but are so often neglected.

Fishes, like human beings, need air to breathe, healthy surroundings and a wholesome, balanced diet.

Fishes breathe air dissolved in water. Air dissolves in water when the two are shaken together or when the surface of the water is large in proportion to the volume. A glass bowl with a small opening is the worst possible repository for fishes *unless aerated with great care*. A broad, shallow trough is better than a deep narrow tank.

Air may be pumped into the water, and there are several useful devices on the market for supplying artificial aeration.

Another good method is to furnish the tank with suitable aquatic plants. Under the influence of sunlight these plants absorb carbon dioxide from the air (and the water) and give off oxygen, of which a certain amount remains in the water. This is breathed in by the fishes, who in their turn exhale carbon dioxide. Thus, like Jack Sprat and his wife in the nursery rhyme, plant and animal life in a well-arranged aquarium are each sustained by that element which is rejected by the other.

However obtained, an adequate air supply is a prime necessity. If the fishes are many or large, they will soon exhaust the available air and rise gasping to the surface.

The primary rule is, therefore: *Don't crowd your tank.*

Clean water is also essential, but care must be taken in its renewal. You cannot simply pour away the dirty water from the tank and fill it up again under the tap. Fishes, as we have seen already, are very sensitive to sudden changes in temperature, and tap water is usually much colder than that in the tank. It is therefore desirable to fill a pail or two and leave them in the room for a couple of hours until their contents have taken on the temperature of the surrounding air. The dirty water may then be *siphoned* out and the fresh water in. Siphoning minimizes disturbance and possible injury to the fish, and is easily the simplest and cosiest way to transfer liquids without splashing.

Fishes in private aquaria are often underfed, and their diet is far from being balanced. Many of the so-called "fish foods" sold in shops are stale and useless.

If you keep goldfish or any others of the Carp family, you should give them bits of brown bread, insects of all kinds (flies, grubs, maggots, gnats, small caterpillars, etc.), small earthworms (or large ones cut in pieces), freshwater shrimps, waterfleas, etc. For "tropical" fishes there are special mixtures prepared and put up by reputable firms, and these may be safely relied on.

Food should be offered in small doses and often; if a large amount is given at one time there are certain to be fragments left uneaten whose decomposition will pollute the water.

Any of you who has a garden can, with very little trouble, treat yourself to a fishpond, which will be at once an ornament and a fascinating hobby. It may be that your garden already boasts of a pool on which water-lilies float. In all probability such a pool is already quite well adapted for stocking with fishes.

It doesn't matter whether your pond is just a depression in the ground or an elaborate structure of brick and concrete, so long as it reaches in some part of it a depth of 18 in. or more. It is not likely that water will freeze to this depth, and there will be always a residue at the disposal of the fishes.

On the bottom there should be 2 or 3 in. (rather more than less) of clean sand and fine gravel.

It is essential that the pond be well garnished with water plants which, if they are to flourish, need plenty of light. On the other hand, a pool is prettier if partly screened by bushes, and fish like the shade. For this purpose a small clump of willow is useful. Broad-leaved plants mean a lot of clearing up of dead leaves in the autumn. On no account must these be left to rot in the pond, and they must be raked away from the surface.

Water-lilies are pretty and popular. When planting them, pay special attention to the instructions given with the roots or you will have no success with them. There are other plants, less decorative but more useful, which will cost only the trouble of gathering them. First of these (and best for the indoor tank) is the Canadian or American Water Weed (*Elodea*), with little leaves in whorls, resembling that well-known pest chickweed, or thyme. It is found in practically every pond or stream and is extremely hardy. It is advisable to fix one end of the stem to a pebble and moor it in the sand of the bottom, but it will grow even if left floating.

This plant is an excellent oxygenator (in strong sunshine you can see little bubbles of oxygen streaming from the leaves), and fishes of the Carp family feed on its buds.

Another useful plant, the *Water Crow's-foot*, is also extremely ornamental. It has pretty white flowers and leaves of two distinct kinds, above the water resembling those of the buttercup and below the surface like fine filaments. This is also a very good supplier of oxygen.

Among floating plants *Duckweed* and *Crystalwort* are valuable both as aerators and as food, and once they have settled down will spread very rapidly—at times too rapidly. They can be picked from most ponds and ditches, together with the less useful but more attractive *Frogbit*, with its rosettes of leaves and glossy three-leaved white blossoms.

All these plants are easily obtained at the cost of a walk in the country with rake and bucket, but if you feel lazy you can buy them very cheaply from aquarium dealers.

Don't put in any fishes until the plants are *well* established. This is an important point, often neglected.

It will be a great help in establishing a balance of life in your pool if, in addition to the plants, you introduce a few small animals who will also provide a first-class diet for your fish. One of the best is the *Freshwater Shrimp*, a lively little creature not unlike the Sandhopper (which you may have noticed on the sea-shore). You will almost certainly find a few of these in every tuft of Elodea you pick out of the water. Another little fellow, the *Freshwater Louse*, is also very useful. These two small creatures are very useful scavengers, and will keep your pool clean. They will also be greatly appreciated by the fish as a toothsome addition to their menu. Another good scavenger is the *Ram's-horn Water Snail*, a dark, coiled snail flattened on one side. It can be found easily enough in ditches and ponds if you scoop up some vegetation and examine the fronds. This snail and others eat up the green slime of algae that forms on the sides of the pond.

Another unsightly kind of algae is made up of an immense number of microscopic plants that grow very profusely (especially in spring) and give to the water the semblance of pea-soup. You will have noticed its appearance in A.R.P. storage tanks. Water so affected is quite wholesome to the animals that dwell in it, but the effect is uninviting and you cannot see anything below the surface. To prevent or cure this pest it is advisable to put into the pool a few freshwater mussels of the smaller kind. The so-called *Duck Mussel* is the best; it doesn't plough up the bottom as its bigger and better-known relative, the *Swan Mussel*, does. Mussels live by sifting small organic particles from the water, thereby filtering it very effectively. You can get Mussels from dealers at very low cost.

Yet another group of very small creatures is needed to put the finishing touches to the arrangement of your pond. You must have a good assortment of *Water Fleas* which, in spite of the disagreeable associations conjured up by the name, are interesting and pretty animals if observed under a good magnifying glass. The three commonest are *Daphnia* (closely resembling a flea), *Cyclops* (usually with two little bags of eggs that look like tails) and *Cypris*. You can buy them from a shop or scoop them up with a jam jar from any small pond or ditch, the dirtier the better. They are very small indeed, and you will only see them by holding your jar of water up to the light. They are a great help in keeping the water clean, and are excellent food for small fishes.

Let me recapitulate a bit. In order to make a success of your fishpond you must first of all start your plants going well. After about a month put in a good number of water fleas, shrimps and mussels, and the right snails, and leave them to establish themselves for at least another month (*not* an autumn or winter month). Last of all, introduce the fishes you have chosen.

Don't think only in terms of Goldfish. Some of the commonest fishes of our ponds and rivers are often more beautiful and more interesting, and are certainly more hardy. Why not try a few small Carp? They can become tame enough to take titbits out of your fingers. Or Rudd, splendid with scarlet and gold? Or Roach, Tench or Gudgeon?

A properly balanced pond, *not* overcrowded, will probably supply enough food for its inhabitants without further provision. It may be as well, however, to give some additional food in the autumn and winter.

If you have a fairly large pool and wish to see your fish increase and multiply, remember that the water must in some places be very shallow, with plenty of Elodea and Water Moss to give

shelter to the fry and enable them to escape their parents'
appetites.

Aquaria indoors and ponds outdoors are fascinating, but if you
wish to enjoy them you must know what you are at. I have
given you a few fundamental instructions; you must do the rest.
Borrow a book on the subject from your Public Library or your
school. (There are many of them, large and small, some remarkably good.) Get a general idea of the subject, then buy the book
that suits you best and go ahead with the aquarium. It will cost
you very little trouble or money (after the first outlay), and will
add tremendously to the interest of your home.

SPECIAL SECTION

★

BRITISH
FRESHWATER AND ESTUARINE
FISHES

GENERAL REMARKS

WHEN you wish to identify an unknown fish, turn first to the Identification Table on page 101. It will save you going through the book.

In some privately owned waters are to be found species of non-British origin, such as the Brook and Rainbow Trout, the Goldfish, the Orfe, the Black Bass and possibly others. They have been artificially introduced, and in such cases the water owners are best able to supply the information needed.

There is no close season at sea. For fresh water there are usually regulations about close seasons and minimum legal sizes of fish; for most waters a fishing licence is also necessary before you start fishing. Regulations vary from one Fishery Board to another, sometimes even from one river to another. You must enquire locally, from anglers, Police or Post Offices. As a rule, the close season for "coarse" fish is from the 15th of March to the 15th of June, both days included. Close seasons for Salmon and Trout are (roughly) the cold months.

A list of technical terms is given at the end of the book, before the general index.

Quotations without mention of author are from Izaak Walton's *Compleat Angler*.

If you want to know more about fish (and I hope you will), look up the little bibliography at the end of the book.

The Fish Department of the Natural History Museum, South Kensington, London, S.W.7, welcomes uncommon, strange, freakish and rare specimens of fish, and you will help scientific research by sending such specimens there. Pass on to the biologists in the High Schools or Universities of your district any useful information about fish. They will know if it is worth bringing before the high ranks of Science. Please *do not* send to South Kensington a small Chub as a giant Dace, or a Wrasse as a "unique tropical fish"; naturalists are kind-hearted people, but they are also very busy, and are not particularly amused when their time is wasted by enquiries that could be avoided if people took the trouble to consult a book, even such an elementary one as this volume.

IDENTIFICATION TABLE

WHEN the fish you want to identify has:

(A) a *flattened shape*—see Flounder (estuarine).

(B) a *snake-like shape*, and has: (*a*) a *round, sucker-like mouth, no pectoral or ventral fins*—see Lampreys; (*b*) normal, *terminal mouth*, and: (1) *one dorsal fin*, no ventral fins—see Eel; (2) *two dorsal fins*, three barbels round the mouth—see Burbot.

(C) *five rows of bony plates* along the body—see Sturgeon (estuarine).

(D) normal shape, *one dorsal fin*, and: (*a*) the fin is *on the middle* of the back, and: (1) the *mouth is small and toothless*—teeth in the throat—*lateral line present*—see Carp family; (2) the mouth has very small teeth—*no lateral line*—see Shads (estuarine); (*b*) the dorsal fin is *near the tail*, over the anal fin: (1) *no spines*, mouth very large—see Pike; (2) *spines before the fins*, fish small—see Sticklebacks.

(E) normal shape, *two dorsal fins:* (*a*) one soft fin in the middle of the back, and a *very small one* (adipose) near the tail—see Salmon family; (*b*) *the first fin is spiky*, the second soft; (1) both fins are *close together*—see Perch family; (2) *fins are apart*—silvery appearance—see Bass (large mouth) or Grey Mullets (small mouth), both estuarine; (3) the fish is small, with a *large head* and large pectoral fins—see Bullhead.

THE LAMPREY FAMILY

WHEN you were told at school that Henry I "died of a surfeit of lampreys," you were probably puzzled; perhaps you did not know what "surfeit" meant, or, if you did, you wondered how anybody could possibly die from overeating. And if you asked what Lampreys were, you were probably told vaguely that it was some kind of fish. A vague classification indeed, because Lampreys are not true "fish." If you examine a Lamprey you will notice that it is *snake-like*, that it has no jaws, *nor paired fins*, nor scales, that *there are seven little slits in a row* behind the eye, and that *the mouth is round and sucker-like*. If you eat a Lamprey you will discover that it is uncommonly good, and that it has just a few bits of gristle instead of countless sharp bones. There are neither pectoral nor ventral fins, only two dorsal and the tail fins. The mouth is round, with many horny teeth and a strong tongue armed with sharp horny spikes. Lampreys are mostly parasitic on fishes: they attach themselves to their victims by means of their sucking lip, and use the tongue to scrape away the flesh of their host, drinking its blood at the same time. Tate Regan quotes the case of a Basking Shark infested by a large number of Sea Lampreys that feasted on the unfortunate giant till it died.

There are two or, according to some zoologists, three British species of Lampreys, differing by the structure of their mouths and the position and shape of the dorsal fins.

The largest is the SEA LAMPREY (*Petromyzon marinus*), usually about 2 ft. in length and occasionally more than 3 ft., with a weight of over 5 lb. The ground colour is yellow, grey or greenish, darker on the back and lighter on the belly, with darker spots and marblings. The first dorsal fin is quite separate from the second, which is *separated from the tail fin only by a notch*. The sucking disc has *numerous rows of teeth covering its entire surface*; the teeth immediately round the mouth opening (above and at the

side) are double; under the mouth there is a ridge, consisting of 6
or 7 teeth, and on the tongue there are several pairs of saw-edged
teeth.

Next in size comes the LAMPERN or River Lamprey (*Petromyzon* or *Lampetra fluviatilis*), that reaches 16 in., but normally
is about 1 ft. in length. It is uniformly brownish or greenish
on the back, the colour fading on the sides; the belly is white or
silvery. The first dorsal fin is separate from the second, which is
almost triangular in shape and *is joined to the tail fin*. The sucking
disc has a fringe of small teeth all round; below the mouth there
is a row of 7 or 8 teeth, but there are *no other teeth* below these;
above the mouth there is a long transversal tooth, above which
you will notice two rows of small single teeth ; on each side
of the mouth there are only three double or treble teeth ; the
tongue bears a single saw-edged tooth with a higher point in
the middle.

The smallest species is the BROOK LAMPREY (*Petromyzon* or
Lampetra planeri), about the size and length of a pencil. It
resembles the Lampern very much, differing mostly because *the
first and second dorsal fins are not separate, the second having a rounded
edge*.

The Brook Lamprey becomes mature immediately after
reaching the adult stage, whereas the Lampern has a sea life during
which the roes are immature. In both species the dorsal fins
come close together at the spawning time. A Lamprey not more
than 6 in. long, and with ripe roes, is sure to be a Brook Lamprey.
If it is still immature at a length of over 6 in., it will be a Lampern;
its dorsal fins will be separate, and will come close together only
when the fish is ready to spawn, by which time it will have
reached a length of 8 in. or more.

The Sea Lamprey spends most of its adult life at sea. The
Lampern does the same, but many individuals remain all their
life in large rivers or lakes, while the Brook Lamprey never
leaves fresh water.

The spawning habits are very similar in the three species. The fish ascend the rivers in summer, pair off, and start preparing a nest in a sandy and gravelly spot by removing the pebbles which they seize by means of their suckers (hence the name, local and scientific, of Stone-suckers) and shift aside, usually downstream. The eggs are laid in the sand, to which they stick, and then they are covered with more sand by the parents. The Lamperns instead of pairing make a co-operative effort in building the nest, from 10 to 50 fish congregating for the purpose. After spawning, the fish are so weakened that they die.

The eggs hatch out in 10 to 15 days. The larvae are quite unlike the adult, and live in mudbanks like a lugworm. The mouth is a slit fringed with very small barbels, the eye is almost invisible, the fins much reduced, and instead of the seven gill-slits there is a thin groove. The larva is called Pride, Mud Lamprey or Blind Lamprey, and changes into the adult after three or four years, when they are a few inches long. Then the young Lampreys begin their swimming existence.

The Sea Lamprey has become an infrequent visitor, and the other two species are far less common and widespread than they used to be, on account of river pollution. In old days Lampreys and Lamperns were much appreciated as a delicacy, either stewed, fried or grilled. I have tasted Lamperns several times on the Continent, and have found them worthy of a "surfeit."

The Sea Lamprey and the larger Lamperns are caught in nets or eel-baskets, usually at night. Occasionally one or two may be caught while in the act of boring into a fish on which they have fastened their teeth. The Prides may be dug out of the mud like worms; they are feeble swimmers, and once dislodged from their burrows are easily caught by hand. Both Prides and small Lampreys are used as an excellent bait for freshwater and sea fish.

18

THE STURGEON (*Acipenser sturio*—Sturgeon family)

THE Sturgeon is one of the few survivors of the ancient group of the "ganoid" fishes so abundant in early geological days. It retains five longitudinal rows of ganoid bony scutes or shields, shaped like a small pyramid, with sharp edges or spines; there is a row on the back, one on each side, and two on the belly. The skin is grey or brown, white on the belly; there is a small dorsal fin a little before the tail. The head is peculiar, with a long snout and a toothless mouth with four barbels in front. The fish grows to a very large size, even 18 ft. in length; a weight of 4 cwt. with a length of 9 or 10 ft. is not uncommon.

The Sturgeon is a sea fish that enters rivers to spawn; it is doubtful whether it does so in British waters, although specimens have been captured as far inland as Shrewsbury and Nottingham. It spawns in large rivers of Continental Europe, and where it is abundant it forms the object of important fisheries. The Caspian Sturgeon is caught in enormous quantities in the Volga; the eggs, which are very numerous (averaging 3 millions in an adult female), yield that costly and over-rated delicacy called caviare, while isinglass of a high quality is prepared from the inner coat of the air-bladder.

The Sturgeon is a slow-moving fish, rooting in the mud for small creatures that it feels with its barbels and sucks up into its mouth. In spite of its sluggishness it is a powerful fish, and anyone lucky enough to capture a good specimen ought to be very careful in handling his prey, because the sharp and hard scutes along the body allow the Sturgeon to inflict serious wounds. A few specimens are caught now and then in British waters, mostly in salmon nets, trawls and seine nets. In those Continental rivers where the fish is common, either nets or harpoons are employed in its capture. The flesh is much appreciated, tasting rather like superfine pork or veal.

Do not forget that if you catch a Sturgeon in Britain the fish does not belong to you but to the Crown, because a greedy mediaeval king prescribed that it is a "royal fish." Your recompense will consist in being able to spread your arms wide in describing your capture without prevaricating.

19

THE SALMON FAMILY (*Salmonidae*)

To many people and for a variety of reasons this is the most interesting family of all; to the housewife, because these fish have excellent flesh and are easy to prepare; to the trade, because they are of great economic importance to fishermen, packers, exporters and dealers; to anglers, because many species afford fine sport;

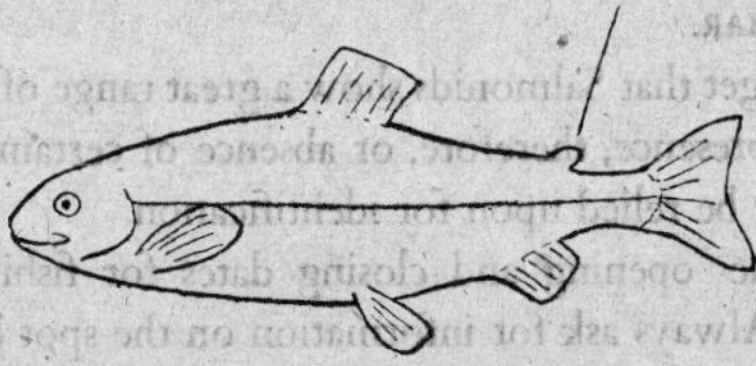

Soft dorsal fin   Adipose fin

Torpedo-shaped body   Ventral fins in
abdominal position

Fig. 4—Typical Salmonid

and lastly to the naturalist, who can lose himself in studying the infinite variety of appearance, coloration and habits to be found in these fish, and have a glorious time arguing interminably with his fellow naturalists about them.

The Salmonids are found in the sea and in fresh waters; many of them in both. They may live high up in mountain streams and lakes or in the depths of the sea (the closely connected Argentines down to 600 fathoms). They are shapely, and usually beautifully coloured and marked. They are also delicious to eat. Small wonder they are such universal favourites.

The members of this family have two characteristics in common: a slender spindle shape, and a small fin without spines or rays, placed on the back, near the tail. This little fin, called *adipose*, is just a little flap, visible even in young specimens 1 in.

long. By this means a Salmonid can be recognized as such at first glance. But when we try to identify the different species, difficulties may be very great. Fig. 4 gives the outline of a typical Salmonid showing the fundamental characteristics of the family. If a fish has an *adipose fin* and has:

(1) A large striped dorsal fin it is a GRAYLING.

(2) A lateral line ending after about 10 scales it is a SMELT (estuarine);

(3) The appearance of a Herring, small mouth and minute teeth, it is a WHITEFISH;

(4) A large mouth with sharp teeth, it may be a SALMON, TROUT or CHAR.

Do not forget that Salmonids show a great range of coloration, and that the presence, therefore, or absence of certain colours or marks cannot be relied upon for identification.

NOTE.—The opening and closing dates for fishing differ a great deal. Always ask for information on the spot before fishing. Most bailiffs, thank Heaven, are very strict.

THE SALMON (*Salmo salar*)

What a lot of books have been written about the Salmon! A few are scientific studies, even fewer are literary essays, many are angling texts, and many, many more are expensive volumes of reminiscences about "big ones" caught in rivers where you, Reader, and I, have little chance to fish. Why so much fuss about this single fish?

Because "the Salmon is accounted the king of freshwater fish," and quite rightly, from every point of view, sporting, culinary, commercial, snobbish. Its life-history still presents several problems to biologists, although its economic importance has made the Salmon an object of well-conducted study for several centuries. Walton himself gives an account of marking experiments, and his report on the fish is exempt from the kind of weird superstitions he quotes in connection with the Pike, the Tench or the Eel.

The life of the Salmon is spent partly in the sea (where it grows) and partly in fresh water (where it spawns and spends its youth). Its migratory habits and mode of life vary a great deal from one river to another, and in this very short account we cannot go into details. Here we must content ourselves with a general outline of the Salmon's history, and anyone who wishes to know exactly what happens in any particular river will have to read a book on the neighbourhood or ask local anglers or water bailiffs for information.

Adult Salmon may enter fresh water at any time of the year, the season preferred varying from river to river. They may be young fish between 3 and 3½ years of age (these are called *grilse*) or older fish coming to spawn for the first time (*maiden Salmon*) or that have spawned before. The nomenclature becomes further complicated by the addition of the season in which the fish runs in from the sea, by its changes in appearance and condition during the spawning season, by the length of time since it entered the river and by occasional fanciful local names. To make matters fairly intelligible to the non-specialist, I will give a short list of the commonest terms. *Fresh-run* is a Salmon that has recently entered a river; it has often small parasitic crustacea ("sea-lice") attached to its skin, which die and fall off after four or five days in fresh water at the utmost. *Clean fish* are the best for the table; they are silvery, with a blue-grey back and small dark spots scattered here and there above the lateral line; the flesh is red, firm and rich in fat; the roes are small. *Unclean fish* are those very near to the spawning time, or that have just spawned; their flesh is pale and flabby, with little fat, their skin thick and spotted, with red or orange marblings in the males ("red fish") and dark in the females ("black fish"). The male's jaws get longer, and the lower one develops a queer "hook" turned upwards. *Kelts* are fish that have spawned, and are on their way back to the sea; they are in very poor condition, very lean, with heads that seem disproportionately large; they are so enfeebled that they often die before reaching the sea, or fall victim to diseases; their flesh is of very poor quality and they ought never to be killed.

Some Salmon (*droppers*) run up rivers in the late winter or early spring, but do not stay and go back to sea, returning later on to fresh water to spawn. The majority enter the estuaries between spring and autumn, and spawn between September and January, mostly in November and December. The fish thus may spend anything from a few days to several months in fresh water before spawning. During this period they are not interested in feeding and their stomachs are empty. When they snatch at the angler's bait (gaudy and beautiful artificial flies, prawns, small fish, spinning lures of infinite variety), they are probably more inspired by curiosity, annoyance or excitement than by hunger. It is possible that an occasional titbit may be eaten, but there is no doubt that adult Salmon do not grow while in fresh water; on the contrary, they lose weight the whole time, even before spawning.

The Salmon is a swift and powerful swimmer, and its capacity for overcoming obstacles on its "run" is famous. The fish can swim with success against rapids, and jump over weirs and small waterfalls. These jumps tend to reach notable dimensions in the tales of people who have seen them. As a matter of fact, even under the best conditions (when the water below the obstacle is deep and quiet) it is doubtful whether the maximum height passes 8 ft.; 6 ft. is a normal figure. The fish jumps in a slanting direction with its body almost straight, and not in a curved position, such as is shown in some pictures, owing to an old idea that the jump was procured by the fish holding its tail in its mouth and releasing in this way a kind of spring. A hooked fish (and not Salmon only; Trout or Bass behave in the same way) may jump out of the water in a curved attitude because it tries to swing itself free from the hook.

The fish swim upstream until they reach the spawning grounds, where the water is fairly shallow and swift, and the bottom gravelly. On their journey they may spend some time resting in pools, especially during spring and summer, and then they are more likely to fall victims to anglers.

Once on the spawning grounds the fish pair off; the female scoops a shallow trench in the gravel, and lays there the ripe portion of her eggs, which are immediately fertilized by the male. The eggs are then covered with gravel pushed over them by the parents, and the spawning operation is started anew, after a short interval, a little higher upstream. This continues until all the eggs have been deposited in the nest, which is called a "redd." During the pairing and spawning period the male fish fight each other, as well as male Trout, with great ardour and determination. Once the reproductive process is over, the fish swim feebly down the sea. These spent fish, called *kelts* or *slats*, are very exhausted, lean and weak; they may recover slightly in the pools of the larger rivers, but they do not begin to feed and grow again until they reach the sea.

The eggs are rather large, being about $\frac{1}{4}$ in. in diameter, of an orange colour and with a tough skin. A female lays about 800–900 eggs for every pound of her weight, a very small figure when compared with the 60,000 or more of the Carp. Many of them are never fertilized; many more are eaten by eels and other fish or by waterfowl. This is not surprising, on account of the long period of incubation, which may last from five weeks to five months, according to the temperature of the water. The fry, or *alevins*, are about $\frac{1}{2}$ in. in length when they hatch out, and spend a month or two hidden among the pebbles of the redd, living on the contents of a small bag (yolk-sac) of nutritive substance, situated on their chests. By the time the yolk-sac has been absorbed the baby fish are about 1 in. long, and begin feeding on their own. In this stage they are called *parr*. Their bodies are marked with seven to eleven dark, oval, vertical, sooty spots ("parr marks," see Plate 3), between which is a small reddish spot; two or three black dots in a row are seen behind the eye, as well as numerous small dark and red dots scattered above the lateral line. The parr live in the shallows, feeding on small shellfish and insect larvae. They rise only too easily to the fly: need I beg my readers to unhook these small fish with the greatest care, and release them gently in the stream?

The parr spend about two years in fresh water, and then turn into *smolts*, assuming a silvery coat similar to that of the adult fish, though in some rivers the parr marks may still show faintly under the silvery colour of the scales. In southern rivers a few parr become smolts after one year, while in northern rivers many wait three years before this change. In northern Norwegian rivers parr wait four or five years before entering the smolt stage. The smolts therefore may be of different sizes, from 5 to 9 in. in length. During the summer months the smolts go down tail first to the sea, snapping at any fly: that is the reason why water bailiffs insist on your fishing "upstream" with your trout flies (if you are a flyfisher you know what I mean—if you are not, it would take too long to explain).

Once the smolts have reached the sea they start following the shoals of sand-eels and young herrings and sprats, feeding greedily on them, and growing at an astonishing rate, so that in about a year they may weigh more in pounds than they weighed in ounces when they first entered salt water. Smolts weigh on an average about 3 oz. and grilse 4 to 5 lb., though very early runners may be a meagre 1½ lb. and late runners over 10 lb. The majority of the grilse run up the rivers a year after leaving them, that is, in June and July. Some of them do not spawn in their first season, and do not visit fresh water until the next winter or spring, spawning in the successive colder months. Others do not enter the rivers until they are from four to six years old ("maiden Salmon"), when they spawn for the first time. It is among these fish, that have never undergone the exhausting experience of spawning, that the biggest and heaviest specimens are found.

The life history of the Salmon has been traced in great detail from the observation of a large number of marked fish, carried out in several countries. It has thus been possible to prove that most Salmon return to spawn in the rivers where they were born. There is a firmly fixed idea that this is the invariable rule. As a matter of fact, Salmon are quite prepared to invade new rivers if opportunity offers. At the mouth of the Ballysodare River, Sligo, there are falls which prevented the ascent of Salmon. In 1840 a fish ladder was constructed there and another one at Collooney a couple of miles higher up. Salmon invaded the three rivers of the Ballysodare basin, where none had ever been before. Salmon have been observed at the mouth of the Thames, and if that river ever ceases to be a poisonous sewer in the last seventy miles of its course it might become celebrated again for the excellence of its Salmon, as it was in Walton's days.

Another important source of information has been the study of scales under the microscope. The Salmon's scales bear concentric rings similar to those seen in the wood of trees. In summer, food is abundant and growth rapid, with wide rings; in winter, growth is slower and the rings are narrow. During the spawning season not only is there no growth but the fish wastes away; this is reflected on the scale by a frayed edge. From the study of these scales it has been possible to see that some fish, in some rivers, spawn only once in their life; others spawn every year, others every two.

The life at sea of the Salmon has been studied by the Norwegian biologist Dahl, but there are still some obscure points. They are caught very seldom in the trawl or in other sea nets. From what information it has been possible to gather they do not appear to go very far from the coast or very deep into the water, and prey on small fish, such as Herrings, Sand Eels or Mackerel.

The size, shape and weight of Salmon show wide variations from one water to another, and one might almost say that there is a special race for every river. The fact is understandable when one considers the tenacity with which Salmon stick to the river of their birth, and the ease with which all members of the Salmon family alter their appearance in different surroundings. If most of the members and descendants of a certain tribe of

Salmon keep for centuries to the same river, the results will tend to approximate to those found among other localized groups of a given species. Generally speaking, big rivers hold larger Salmon. In some waters fish over 15 lb. would be considered large, while in others (the Shannon, for example) they would be merely average. The Tay, the Wye, and the Shannon are well known for the exceptionally large Salmon they have yielded. The waters of the neighbouring rivers Shin, Carsely and Oykel in Sutherland mingle in the small Dornoch Firth, and so do the smolts from them, all alike and about the same weight. But when they come back as grilse or Salmon, the fish of the Shin are much bigger though not so well shaped as those of the other two rivers.

Salmon compete with Pike in size, both in fact and fiction. Regarding the latter, the record set by an ancient Irish chronicle has never been beaten. In the *Chronicum Scotorum* for the year 1109 it is stated that "at Limerick a Salmon was caught, twelve feet in length, twelve hands in breadth, and with a neck fin three hands and two fingers long." I love those "two fingers" in the description of a fish the size of a Blue Shark (as it may have been). Calderwood mentions one of 103 lb. caught in the Firth of Forth in 1901. The largest specimen angled with rod and line weighed 64 lb. and was hooked by a girl, in 1922, in the Tay. Very few other fish over 60 lb. have been caught on rod and line, but nets have many times taken fish of larger size, such as 84 lb. in the Tay, 80 lb. (found dead) in the Wye and 72 lb. in the Shannon. Nets account for a much greater number of Salmon than do rods (possibly ten times greater). The economic importance of the Salmon may be imagined, considering that before the 1939 war three and a half million pounds a year of these fish were sold in Billingsgate market, apart from large quantities sold or consumed locally. If we add the sums paid for fishing licences, rents of waters and fishing lodges, Salmon tackle, first-class railway tickets, lawyers' fees for legal squabbles and dozens of other sources of expense, we can understand why the Salmon is responsible for such a large turnover of money. Salmon angling is definitely an expensive sport, unless you are lucky enough to live in some remote Scottish or most Irish districts, when it is another story.

It is *very easy* to confuse Salmon with Trout at all periods of development. That grand fish expert, Frank Buckland, told a story about some Scots stake-net fishermen who had taken an odd-looking fish. One said it was a kelt, another believed it was a Sea Trout, a third thought it was a Bull Trout. "Never mind," concluded the headman, "it will be a Salmon on the London market. Put him into the ice-box."

Let us begin with the parr stage, during the first year, when the young fish are about 3 or 4 in. long (Fig. 5). The Salmon

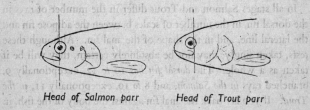

Head of Salmon parr   Head of Trout parr

Fig. 5

parr has three black spots, more or less marked, on the gill-cover behind the eye; dark pectoral fins; the hind edge of the lip (maxillary, to be exact) reaches an imaginary vertical line descending from the middle of the eye; the narrowest part of the body a little before the tail fin measures about one-tenth of the length of the fish's body (tail fin not included). The Trout parr has no series of spots behind the eye, a greater number of coloured dots on its sides, pectoral fins more or less orange, a large mouth, (so that the inner edge of the lip reaches a vertical line behind the pupil of the eye), a greater depth of the portion before the tail (one-eighth of the total length of the body, instead of one-tenth as in the Salmon parr).

The greatest difference between the two-year-old parr and

smolt of the two species consists in the colour of the pectoral fins (orange in the Sea Trout smolt, which has also anal, caudal and adipose fins touched with orange—the Salmon smolt has dark pectoral and pale ventral and anal fins), and in the size of the mouth, which again is larger in the Trout. Drawing an imaginary vertical line from the end of the lip, this line would just touch the posterior edge of the pupil in the Salmon smolt, and almost the posterior edge of the eye in the Trout.

Grilse and Sea Trout are very similar in appearance, although not in habits. They may be distinguished once more by the relative size of the mouth. Drawing the usual vertical line from the end of the lip, it would touch the end of the eye or very little beyond, while in the Sea Trout it would be well behind the eye.

In all stages Salmon and Trout differ in the number of rays in the dorsal fin, in the number of scales between the adipose fin and the lateral line, and in the shape of the anal fin. Although these tests, taken singly, may not be absolutely certain, they will be if taken as a whole. The *dorsal fin has* 10 *to* 12, exceptionally 9, branched rays *in the Salmon*, and 8 *to* 10, exceptionally 11, *in the Trout*. If you lay back the anal fin against the body of the fish, in *the Salmon the last ray* (nearest to the tail) generally *sticks out farther than the longest* in the fin; the opposite is the rule for the *Trout*, in which the *longest ray* of the anal fin *sticks out more than the last*, always when the fin is laid down flat. As a last test count the scales between the back edge of the adipose fin and the lateral line, going forward and downwards (see Fig. 6); *in the Salmon* there are *from* 10 *to* 13 *scales*, and *in the Trout from* 13 *to* 16, exceptionally 12. All tests founded on coloration may help if accompanied by considerable knowledge of the fish of a certain district, but such tests are not reliable if taken by themselves. The colour of the flesh is of no value at all, as it varies enormously with locality, season, size and age of fish: do not forget that the flesh of some Trout may be bright pink and that of a kelt whitish.

The flesh of "clean" Salmon is among the most nourishing and tasty of all fish. Whether steamed, grilled, baked, hot or cold, it is delicious. There is no need to suggest special recipes: why, even an Irish cook could not fail to prepare Salmon in an appetizing way.

The Pacific Salmon sold so extensively in tins is not the British kind. There are five species of Pacific Salmon, although from the names on the labels one might think there were ten times as many. The quality of these tins varies, not only with the species

Fig. 6—Scales in tail of Salmon
(Specially drawn by E. Friedlander)

of fish, but even more with the condition of the fish when caught and canned. The American and Canadian Governments have done much in supervising this industry: would it be too presumptuous on my part to suggest that the label, instead of fancy names, should bear a quality grading or the official or scientific name of the species inside the tin, as well as a simple statement of the fish's condition?

I am quite aware that this short chapter on the Salmon is totally inadequate, and therefore beg my readers to turn to one of the several excellent works on the life of the Salmon, such as those written by W. L. Calderwood, P. D. Malloch and J. A.

Hutton; Henry Williamson's *Salar the Salmon* is a very popular work on the subject.

In the good old quiet days, when news was scarce in summer, newspapers often published reports about wondrous huge fish seen in the Thames, usually between Abingdon and Oxford. These monsters were generally described as specimens of the non-migratory Salmon or *Huchen* of the Danube (*Hucho hucho*), introduced many years ago into the Thames. I have never read any reliable statement of captures, and I do not forget that Thames Trout run large. Several of those reports came from under-graduates boating on the river, and—well, I have been a student myself.

THE TROUT (*Salmo trutta*)

I experienced one of the greatest thrills of my young days when my father bought a dozen Trout from a local professional fisher-man. Those Trout, caught in a neighbouring stream, did not fit the description of any of the ten species of Trout in my textbook! The dream of every naturalist, be he nine or ninety, had become reality for me: I had found a *new species!* I supposed our district was too much out of the way for biologists, and therefore its possibilities were still unexplored. Why, there might be *more* new species! For three months I plagued everybody who caught Trout, and I fished every water most assiduously. And as it is always easy to find what you want to find, I collected half a dozen new species, complete with Celto-Latin names from the streams or lakes of their origin (names as monstrous as any Graeco-Latin horror coined by scientists). My luck was too great and made me suspicious. When I found that, in the same lake, Trout differed if caught on one side instead of the other, and that fish in the same river varied according to the stretch they in-habited, I came most regretfully to the conclusion that there was only *one* kind of Trout, and that this fish ought to be called, in my restrained Victorian speech, a very naughty fraud, guilty of cheating even textbook-writing naturalists.

Fish experts, with a great weight of evidence before them, have come to the conclusion to which a boy had been forced in his disappointment. From the ten species described by Günther, we have come down in thirty years to the single one of Tate Regan. The most stubborn "species" was the Sea Trout, that has the appearance and mode of life of the Salmon rather than of the Brown Trout. But even this last stronghold had to fall when some river Trout, out of a consignment sent to New Zealand to stock its rivers, went down to sea and became Sea Trout. Major Ashley-Dodd reports that once he stocked with herlings (young Sea Trout) a newly filled loch that was entirely cut off from any fish invasion. The herlings grew and multiplied, but as Brown Trout, rather similar to the Loch Leven type. The capacity of Trout for altering their appearance from one water to another is almost incredible. The general colour may vary from pale grey and silver to almost black, the markings from a few blackish dots to a great number of spots of several colours and sizes, the weight of an adult fish from 3 oz. to almost 50 lb. Day quotes the case of two small lakes in Inverness-shire stocked at the same time with Trout from Loch Morar; a few years later not only the fish of the two lakes were greatly different externally, but the flesh of one lot was white and that of the other pink.

Trout live, have lived or might live in any water of the British Isles, except those too muddy and stagnant or too poisoned by chemicals or dirt. They are found in two principal forms, the Sea Trout and the Brown Trout, under a vast number of local names, a few of which will be given.

We shall begin with the *Sea Trout*, not because it is considered the more aristocratic of the two, but because its appearance and habits are nearer to those of the Salmon, which we have just described. The Sea Trout is very much like a grilse or small Salmon, that is, silvery with a darker back. Its sides are usually spotted with a greater number of dots and X-shaped marks than those of the grilse or Salmon, and the tail is not forked. It does not roam so far out to sea as the Salmon, and prefers to keep near the shore and close to the estuaries. The farther northwards one goes the more abundant is this Trout, which is quite common in shoals on the coasts of the Scottish islands and northern Scotland, while not particularly frequent in Channel rivers, and totally absent in the Mediterranean. The diet of the Sea Trout is like the Salmon's, and consists of small fish, shrimps and other crustacea, worms, etc. It may be angled from the shore or from boats, using either artificial flies or natural baits, but it is rather shy, and success is much more likely to go to the seine fisherman than to the rod angler. The Sea Trout spawns usually a little earlier than the Salmon of the same river, between September and January, mostly in October and November. The "run" into fresh water is generally restricted to a period between May and November, the first fish in the rivers being, as a rule, smaller than those entering the same river in the autumn. Not only does the Sea Trout spend less time in fresh water, but it continues to feed while there, in contrast to the Salmon. It is therefore easier to catch, and at the same time a much more sporting fish, weight by weight, than its bigger brother, often weakened by a prolonged fast. The favourite lure is an artificial fly similar to the kind used for Salmon, but much smaller. Fly-fishing for Sea Trout at dusk or at night in the pool of an estuary is one of the most thrilling experiences that an angler can have.

The spawning habits are practically the same as those of the Salmon. The males develop a slight hook on the lower jaw, but not on the grotesque scale of the Salmon. The development of the eggs, of the fry and of the parr is like the Salmon's. The smolts (often called Orange-fins) descend to the sea, but do not go there till after spending some time in the estuaries. Their growth is not so rapid, and after a full year in the sea they reach a weight from 2 to 3 lb., much less than a Salmon of the same age. Some of the young Trout may ascend the streams to spawn in the autumn, after having spent only a few months in the sea or in the estuary. They weigh under 1 lb., and are locally called Peel, Herling, Blacktail or White Trout. Some of these names are applied also to the older fish, whose weight may vary from 1½ lb. to almost 50 lb. (as captured in the Tweed). The larger specimens enjoy another assortment of names, such as Sea Trout, Finnock, Sewen, Truff, Scurf, Bull Trout, Round-tail, Whitling, Grey Trout, etc., disregarding names in Gaelic and Welsh.

The flesh may be white, cream or pink, and, as a rule, of a very high quality if the fish is in good condition.

In large estuaries or brackish lochs may be found a variety of Trout intermediate between the sea and the brown types. This *Estuary Trout* has received several local names, such as Bull Trout, Slob Trout, Galway or Orkney Trout (the last two being considered two distinct species by Günther). These fish look like Sea Trout that have retained some of the peculiarities of the Brown type: they are more or less silvery, with black and *red* spots on their sides. They may reach a large size, but they usually do not enjoy a high reputation as food.

The commonest and most widely distributed type is the "Brown" Trout of lakes, rivers and mountain streams. Its colour may range from silver to black; *it may even be brown*. The back is rather dark (from olive to purple black), the sides usually golden with many spots, black, brown, red, large or small, round, oval, X-shaped, sometimes with a ring of a different shade. The lower part may be white, grey, cream, yellow or pinkish. Trout transferred from one water to another may change very much. For instance, the beautiful Loch Leven fish, silvery like a Sea Trout and with flesh like that of Salmon, when reared in hatcheries and transferred to other waters have become commonplace Brown Trout. In large lakes and rivers they may reach a big size; the record fish caught in Britain by rod and line (in Loch Awe) weighed 39½ lb. The abundance and size of Trout depend on many elements, such as cleanliness of the water, amount of oxygen available, abundance or scarcity of food, presence of enemies (such as carnivorous fishes, especially Pike, or fish-eating or spawn-eating birds). If food and enemies are both scarce, a brook may be full of adult Trout (that

is, without parr marks) as small and easy to catch as Gudgeon.
I must add at this point that although the presence of parr marks
("sooty fingers" on the sides) is nearly always a sign that the
Trout is young, there is a race of these fish in a loch in Suther-
landshire that retains the parr marks even in the adult stage, just
as Char often do.

Trout are not easy to see in lakes, except when they come near
the shore, unless they are "rising" to swallow flies on the surface
of the water. In clear streams they are easily seen, provided one
approaches the water with some care. Then Trout may be seen
either in rocky pools, or along the bank, or behind a stone that
protects them from the flood. The speckled sides and straight-
cut tails will reveal the identity of the fish.

The spawning habits of the Brown Trout are similar to those
of the sea type. Gravelly shallows and brooks are preferred.

The food of Trout is varied. While the young or small
specimens keep to a diet of worms, insect larvae, flies, small
snails, crustacea and the fry of fish, the larger fish become very
predaceous, and their choice of food (size apart) is similar to that
of the Pike. Their jaws become longer and sharper, their mouths
larger, their eyes smaller in proportion. Then the chief items of
their diet are small fish, including their younger brethren, together
with any other animal small enough to be eaten. I mean *any*; a
friend of mine found a mouse in the stomach of a Trout, and
"John Bickerdyke" had a similar experience. The greedy
appearance of such large fish, rather unlike that of the smaller
and normal specimens of brook and river, inspired zoologists in
years gone by to raise them to the status of a distinct species,
appropriately called *Salmo ferox*. There is one period in the year
when all Trout (and many other fish too) partake almost exclusively of a special titbit, the Mayfly. When these long-tailed and
clumsy insects appear on the water, all Trout, from the largest to
the smallest, forget all other interests to gorge themselves on this
delicacy.

Fishing for Trout is the principal aim of most anglers in Wales,

Scotland, Ireland, Devon and Cornwall. It is also the principal, or maybe the only, interest of a few people who have nothing better to do, and who have raised this excellent sport to the absurd degree of a snobbish "art," full of fads and bunkum. Trout are a first-class fish for delicate taste, sporting qualities, varied and beautiful appearance. They may be angled for in very pleasant ways. That is all. Trout in some very clear streams of central and southern England are cunning and shy, and difficult to catch with the artificial fly unless one is careful, patient and skilful: those same crafty fish will fall easily to a worm if the water is coloured. A good Roach in public waters remains much more difficult to hook in whatever condition the river is. In most Welsh, Scottish and Irish waters Trout are angled by children, and may be as easy to catch as small Perch. So easy that I must plead for them. Young Trout are so greedy and careless that they will gobble up any maggot or worm passing by, especially if rain has coloured the stream, and if you use such baits you will catch numbers of small fish, many of which will have to be killed because caught in the throat or in the gills. Please, *never* fish for Trout with a worm, unless the water is crystal clear; in all other circumstances keep to the fly or to spinning. There would be many more Trout about if some people were not stupidly selfish.

Now I should like to give you, Brother "Coarse" Angler, a little advice. Why do you, and so many of your brethren, regard fly-fishing as something wonderful, reserved by Providence to "your betters"? I have been embarrassed sometimes when a first-class bottom fisher, whose skill I admired without hope of equalling, has regarded me, a fourth-rate fly-fisherman, with respectful awe, simply because I angled with a fly. Believe me, fly-fishing is neither expensive nor particularly difficult. You do not need a grand rod: you could get before the war a good fly rod at the same price as a good "coarse fishing" one, and the rest of the tackle was not dear. Get a friend or another club member to give you a lesson, or learn by yourself with a book and plenty of practice. Wet-fly fishing is easier, but as soon as you can cast accurately you can take up the dry fly, that will enable you to aim at a certain determined fish, a sport that will never cease to thrill you. You are probably a very good caster already with your stiff rod, and you will pick up the other attainment quickly. Fly-fishing requires patience and skill, two qualities you have already, and which do not ask for bank balances or titles. You may angle not only for Trout, but also for Roach, Dace, Chub and Rudd, and roam about without being fixed to one spot on the bank. Give fly-fishing a try, and you will be surprised to find you can master it so easily. You might perhaps come to the conclusion that it needs less skill than bottom fishing, and that landing half-pounders on 3x gut is nothing when you have been accustomed to land pounders and more on 6x. You might end with saying that there is a lot of humbug about fly and Trout fishing. And, as a matter of fact, there is.

In some rivers it is illegal to kill Trout below a certain length, which is 12 in. in the Lea and 16 in. in the Thames. These minimum lengths and the open seasons vary from one district to another, and anglers must get local information before fishing.

An approximate idea of the weight of a Trout may be obtained from its length. For instance, when 8 in. long the fish is about 3½ oz. in weight; when 10 in. not much more than 7 oz.; at 1 ft., ¾ lb. or little more; at 15 in. about 1½ lb.; at 18 in. about 2½ lb., and at 20 in. about 3½ lb.

Brown Trout from gravelly waters are fine-flavoured, but their taste may become unpleasant in other places. At a formal dinner in one of the best London restaurants I was served with un-doubted Trout. After the first mouthful I looked again at the fish, which tasted like Chub, and at my neighbours', in time to see several of them put down their forks after the first taste. It was not the cook's fault, but the fish were uneatable. In such a case, there is little to be done. Luckily, in most cases Trout are so good that any cook cannot fail to make a dainty dish of them.

THE RAINBOW TROUT (*Salmo irideus*)
Plate 3

If you "talk fish" with an American you may soon discover a fresh proof of the fact that the two of you are not really speaking the same language. In America, Char are called Trout and Trout are "Salmon-Trout"; thus Americans give the rather unsatisfactory name of "Speckled Trout" to a fine species of Char that, when introduced in Britain, received the even more unsatisfactory name of "Brook Trout" (see page 130), a label already often applied to the Brown Trout. It is all very confusing, but to be expected when dealing with such an erratic tribe as the Salmonids. American naturalists have their headaches over their ever-changing species (or varieties) of Trout (Salmon-Trout, I mean), as we have over our European varieties (or maybe species).

One of these American species, the Rainbow Trout, has been introduced into many British waters, and has become a great favourite with anglers for its hardy stamina, beautiful appearance, sporting qualities and delicate taste. It resembles our Brown Trout in appearance and habits, but may be distinguished by the *numerous dark spots on its tail fin*, which is slightly forked, and by a red iridescent lateral band with red blotches; the slight "rainbow" coloration of the Brown Trout is not comparable to the brilliant play of colour of its American cousin, and cannot be confused with it.

The biggest fault of the Rainbow is its "salmon" instinct to go down to the sea; once there it takes a silvery Sea Trout dress, but shows no desire to return into British streams, possibly because of pollution. Therefore, unless it has been placed in landlocked waters, the Rainbow disappears after some time, and the disappointed owner has to start restocking. It has prospered and multiplied in New Zealand and South America, where it had been introduced, and where (as well as in its native waters) fish of 6 and 8 lb. are to be found; in Britain a two-pounder is a good specimen. A Rainbow of 17 lb. 10 oz. was caught in Tasmania in 1933.

The Rainbow is markedly different from our Trout in spawning habits: it lays in early spring a much greater number of smaller eggs. Possibly on account of their reduced size, these eggs are not so hardy as those of the Brown Trout, and the artificial hatching and rearing of Rainbows may be a rather chancy business.

THE CHAR GROUP (*Genus Salvelinus*)

The Char is represented in Britain by a large number of very like species (or varieties, according to some zoologists), and by an imported American one, the Brook Trout. The similarity between the various types is so great that ichthyologists have recognized anything from six (Günther) to fifteen species (Tate Regan). The modern tendency is to accept the larger number, in contrast to the attitude adopted in classifying Trout. The differences between several of the species are so slight that only a specialist would be able to discover them. We shall give here the localities where the different species are to be found, and that will be the easiest way to distinguish them.

Char are very similar in external appearance to the Trout with which they share the mountain lakes that are their usual home. The scales in Char are smaller and more numerous than in Trout and Salmon. There are *no black or brown spots on the Char*, only red, orange or white being present, often below the lateral line only. The back is rather dark, varying from greenish brown to bluish black, fading into silver white or orange on the belly. In the breeding season the males become deep red on their under parts, giving rise to the belief that they are a different species. The most important difference will be seen by opening the mouth of the fish and observing its palate. In the Salmon and Trout there is a bony ridge in the middle of the roof of the mouth, usually with a row or two of teeth. In the Char this bone (vomer) is hollow instead of being ridged, and has only a small protruding cluster of teeth in front.

The size, coloration, breeding season and feeding habits of the Char vary widely with the locality they inhabit, even more than those of the Trout. The maximum weight reached in the British Isles does not surpass 3 lb. (In places the fish are only a few inches in length and ounces in weight.) In some localities they prefer the surface and feed on flies, while in others they haunt the deeper waters and feed on crustacea. Spawning habits are similar to those of the Salmon and Trout; the fish lay their eggs in redds in shallow water, the young develop in a similar way and bear parr marks on their sides.

The WINDERMERE CHAR (*Salvelinus willughbii*) is the most abundant, widespread and best known of the group. The mouth is slightly oblique, at the end of the snout, the lower jaw not more than two-thirds of the head, and there are from 160 to 200 scales in a longitudinal series along the lateral line. It also reaches the largest size, being from 10 to 12 in. long and occasionally more. It is fished by netting and by spinning with a Devon minnow or similar small artificial bait in rather deep water. It is found in several lakes of the Lake District (Windermere, Buttermere and Coniston, Ennerdale, Crummock, Wast, Lowes and Goat's Waters); varieties differing mostly in size and coloration live in several Scottish lochs (Grannoch, Dungeon, Doon, Fada of Uist, Builg, Bruiach, Borollan, Loyal, Baden and Morie).

The HAWESWATER CHAR (*Salvelinus lonsdalii*) differs from the Windermere by its smaller size (6 to 7 in. and about 3 oz. in weight), and the greater length of its lower jaw (more than two-thirds of head). It feeds at the surface on flies. It used to live in Ullswater, but it has probably been destroyed by pollution of the stream where the fish used to spawn; now it is found only in Haweswater.

The STRUAN CHAR (*Salvelinus struanensis*) is found in Loch Rannoch (Perthshire) and possibly in other lakes of the Tay basin. It has a blunt snout with mouth opening below it, feeble teeth, eight or nine branched rays in the dorsal fin and from 158 to 189 scales counted immediately above the lateral line. It reaches a length of about 8 or 9 in. and is a bottom feeder.

The HADDY or KILLIN CHAR (*Salvelinus killinensis*) is deeper then the Struan; it has a longitudinal line of scales ranging between 180 and 220 in number, and a dorsal fin with ten or eleven branched rays; it reaches a much greater size, up to 16 in. It inhabits Loch Killin in Inverness-shire, and possibly also Loch Roy.

The LARGE-MOUTHED CHAR (*Salvelinus maxillaris*), from a loch near Ben Hope and perhaps also from Loch Stack in Sutherland, is characterized by a very large mouth extending well beyond the eye, by bright colours and few orange spots, mostly below the lateral line. Average size about 10 in.

MALLOCH'S CHAR (*Salvelinus mallochi*) from Loch Scourie in Sutherland may reach a foot in length, is covered with numerous light spots, has a small head with a small mouth, and a longitudinal series of scales numbering from 188 to 200.

The ORKNEY CHAR (*Salvelinus inframundus*) used to live in Loch Hellyal in Hoy and was the only Char inhabiting the Orkneys. None has been seen for many years, and it is probably extinct.

The SHETLAND CHAR (*Salvelinus gracillimus*) is the only Char of the Shetlands, and it is found in Loch Girlsta. It has a very slender body, a blunt snout and large fins. Average length 8 in.

The TORGOCH (*Salvelinus perisii*) or Welsh Char lives in three lakes near Llanberis in Caernarvonshire and in Llyn Corsygedol in Merionethshire. It has a pointed snout with a long lower jaw, large fins and large mouth. Its length is about 9 in. and average weight 5 oz. It can be fished with the fly or with a worm; the best season is late summer.

COLE'S CHAR (*Salvelinus colii*) inhabits many Irish lakes in several districts from Kerry to Donegal. It has been found in Loughs Currane, Gortyglass, Conn, Cullen, Inagh, Derryclare, Corrib, Mask, in several small lakes of Connemara and Mayo,

ANGEL-FISH

These two illustrations show the
effects of Protective Coloration

PLAICE

BRITISH FRESHWATER FISHES

YOUNG TROUT (RAINBOW)

PIKE

CRUCIAN CARP

TENCH

GUDGEON

MINNOW

DACE

ROACH

BLEAK

SILVER BREAM

SPINY LOACH

PERCH

BULLHEAD

THREE-SPINED STICKLEBACK

and in the Loughs of Eask and Derg of Donegal. This Char is very similar to the Windermere Char, but its scales are larger, so that there are from 138 to 168 along the lateral line. In the larger lakes it grows to a foot in length, but in the small lakes it does not reach more than 8 in.

GRAY'S CHAR (*Salvelinus grayi*) lives in Lough Melvin, Fermanagh, where it is called "Freshwater Herring," and differs from Cole's Char in having a deeper and more compressed body and larger scales (from 128 to 162 in a longitudinal series); its flesh is white and insipid, unlike that of other Char. Its length is about 10 to 12 in.

TREVELYAN'S CHAR (*Salvelinus trevelyani*) has a longer head than Cole's Char, a pointed snout with strong teeth, and a narrow forehead. It has been found in Lough Finn in Donegal, and may be present in other neighbouring loughs.

SCHARFF'S CHAR (*Salvelinus scharffi*) is found in Lough Owel in Westmeath, and may also be present in the neighbouring loughs of Ennel, Eaghish, Drumland and in Lough na Brach. It can be distinguished from Cole's Char by its sharper snout, smaller and more oblique mouth, round body and smaller scales (up to 186 in a longitudinal line). The colour is more silvery. It can be fished with a wet fly rather deep in the water. The usual weight is from 1 to 2 lb.

The COOMASAHARN CHAR (*Salvelinus fimbriatus*) from Lough Coomasaharn in Kerry has large eyes, a very narrow forehead and long gill-rakers (projections on the inner part of the gills; see page 21), 18 or 19 in number, instead of from 11 to 16 as in the other Irish Chars.

The BLUNT-SNOUTED CHAR (*Salvelinus obtusus*) is characterized by a short and round snout and by a rather flat and narrow forehead. Its scales are fairly large (from 142 to 166 along lateral line). It reaches a length of about 8 in., and has been found in Loughs Luggala, Tay, Dan, Killarney and Acoose. It is probably present in other loughs of Southern Ireland.

Our knowledge of British Chars is still rather sketchy on

account of their mode of living. With the exception of the Windermere, Cole's and Welsh Char in the lakes listed above, any information about these fish, as well as specimens with details of capture, will be welcomed by the Natural History Museum, South Kensington, London, S.W.7, or by the Natural History Department, Ard Mhusaeum na h-Eireann, Dublin.

To the list of the Char we may add the so-called BROOK TROUT (*Salvelinus fontinalis*), an American species introduced into Europe about sixty years ago. It has disappeared from the rivers, either because not hardy enough or because it has found its way to the sea. Specimens may yet survive in some small lakes in Southern Scotland, but, as a rule, it has failed to acclimatize itself. It reaches usually a pound in weight, though in America it is much heavier. It can be distinguished from Trout and native Char by the mottled coloration of the back and of the fins; the tail is usually barred with dark streaks.

THE WHITEFISH GROUP (*Genus Coregonus*)

What has been said for the Char group can be repeated for the Whitefish. They are very alike, they have a very local distribution and are generally little known. Just as for the Char, the easiest and safest way to distinguish them is to know their origin, and we shall give, therefore, only a cursory description of the different species. (Tate Regan's book is again the best to consult for further information.)

The general external appearance of all Whitefish is very much like that of Herring, but they can be distinguished immediately by the small adipose fin near the tail, typical of all the Salmon family, and by the presence of a lateral line. The presence of the adipose fin distinguishes them also from the silvery species of the Carp family that resemble them. They have from 66 to 90 scales along the lateral line.

The larger species are occasionally caught by anglers when fly-fishing, but the greater proportion is netted. All the Whitefish are very dainty eating and much appreciated.

The POWAN (*Coregonus clupeoides*) or Fresh-water Herring lives in Loch Lomond and Loch Esk. It is one of the largest of the group, being usually about 1 ft. in length and often approaching a weight of 2 lb. In Loch Esk sizes are smaller. They may be seen in shoals near the shore in the early morning or late evening.

The SCHELLY (*Coregonus clupeoides stigmaticus*) is a variety of the Powan distinguished by small black specks on back and sides. It is fairly abundant in Haweswater, but rare in the Red Tarn and in Ullswater, probably owing to pollution of the stream feeding the lake. Maximum length 15 in.

Another variety of the Powan inhabits Lake Bala in Wales. It is called the GWYNIAD (*Coregonus clupeoides pennantii*). In appearance, size and mode of life it is like the two preceding fishes.

Three closely allied forms are found in Ireland. The commonest and best known is the POLLAN (*Coregonus pollan*) of Lough Neagh, which is netted in large numbers and occasionally sold on the English market. They feed on small shellfish and larvae, and on some occasions have been taken on the fly. The average size is 9 in. and weight about 6 oz., although much larger specimens have been caught.

The LOUGH ERNE POLLAN (*Coregonus pollan altior*) is on the average slightly larger than the Lough Neagh form, but is not so abundant. It is netted for the market, but not regularly.

The SHANNON POLLAN (*Coregonus pollan elegans*) lives in the lakes connected with the River Shannon, especially in the largest Loughs (Derg and Ree), but is not very common. In Lough Derg in a period of four years 1,469 Pollan were netted; the best fish was 1 lb. 3 oz., and the average weight 6 oz.

Reports of Pollan from other Irish lakes need confirmation.

The LOCHMABEN VENDACE (*Coregonus vandesius*) is found in the Castle and Mill Lochs near the Scottish town of Lochmaben. It has the appearance of a Bleak or a small Herring, but the adipose fin near the tail distinguishes it from the other two fishes.

It is about 8 or 9 in. long. It used to be netted in large numbers, but for many years the catch has been small and infrequent. Its mode of life is like that of the other Whitefish.

The CUMBERLAND VENDACE (*Coregonus vandesius gracilior*) is very similar in all respects to the Lochmaben form, but it is more slender. It inhabits Derwentwater and Bassenthwaite; specimens are scarce, and they are caught only on rare occasions, especially in the latter lake.

The HOUTING (*Coregonus oxyrhynchus*) is characterized by a pointed snout projecting a good deal above the mouth. It grows to a length of 16 in. It is a marine species, frequenting the German and Danish coasts of the North Sea, and ascending the rivers to spawn. It is rare in Britain, where only occasional specimens have been found in English rivers, like the Colne and the Medway.

THE GRAYLING (*Thymallus thymallus*)

I know I'll get into trouble with some people simply by mentioning this fish. You see, there are Grayling fanatics, of a positive and negative kind, if I may say so. The positive ones have as the summit of their dreams a few weeks in the autumn on the Teme. The negative ones are Trout addicts who cannot think of the Grayling without a surge of hatred, and charge it with every possible crime. The former are sure to blame me for giving their fish such a short mention; the latter will swear at me because I can talk of their enemy without swearing. Timidly suggesting that these two groups of enthusiasts should omit this chapter, I will say that the Grayling is absent from Ireland and rather locally distributed in Britain. It has been artificially introduced in many waters in England and Scotland, but in many of them it did not thrive. The Grayling is much more difficult to please than the Trout, although many streams are inhabited by both species. They like running water, and therefore do not stay in lakes, but it must not be too cold; the stream must be clean, sandy or gravelly, with swift shallows between deeper and quieter pools. The tributaries of the Severn and the "chalk streams" of Hampshire hold the most and the best Grayling.

In spite of the clear streams it inhabits, it is not very easy to observe the Grayling, because, unlike the Trout, it keeps near the bottom, and when it rises at a fly it sinks down immediately afterwards. It is only in early summer, when the fish seek highly oxygenated water to recover after spawning, that one may see shoals of Grayling in the shallows, where they may be identified by the large striped dorsal fin.

Flies, insect larvae and nymphs, freshwater shrimps and other small crustacea, worms and the fry of fish are the fundamental items of its diet.

The Grayling is probably the most beautifully coloured British fish. Its appearance, when dead, is not striking: slaty on the back, silvery on the sides with a few black spots and numerous longitudinal grey lines, it gives but the remotest idea of the indescribable feast of colours of the living fish, on which all shades from deep purple to shimmering pink may be admired. The little adipose fin and the very large rounded and striped dorsal fin make the Grayling quite unmistakable. The mouth is rather small, with little teeth. The eye is remarkable for its deep blue, pear-shaped pupil. The young fish keep parr-marks on their sides but are recognizable by the big dorsal fin; they are called pinks (a name given also to the Minnow) or shuts. Grayling may reach a weight of 5 lb. (one of that weight was found in an eel basket near Shrewsbury); the heaviest caught by rod and line (on the Wiltshire Wylye in 1883) was 4 lb. 9 oz. Unfortunately such fish are exceptional; a 1-lb. Grayling is a good fish, and any over 2 lb. has a chance to end in a glass case.

The Grayling, unlike other members of the Salmon family, is a spring spawner (from March to May), a fact that puts it into the category of "coarse fish," although in every other aspect it is a "game fish." The fish pair and lay their eggs in redds scooped out of gravel, as do Trout or Char. The eggs are rather large and not very numerous, a few thousand in the case of a good-sized fish. The fry hatch out in a couple of weeks.

This fish may be angled on the bottom, like Roach or Perch (using as bait maggots or small worms), or with dry and wet flies. Whenever possible, I strongly recommend the latter method: use rather small flies, same patterns as used for Trout, and even if you fail to hook your fish at the first rise it will probably return to your fly. Sometimes Grayling take to feeding on very small creatures (water fleas or tiny nymphs), and then they disregard any other food, including that on your hook. You may then feel like entering the ranks of the Grayling's enemies, forgetting its sporting qualities.

Grayling are slightly heavier than Trout of the same length; keep in mind, however, that the Grayling is out of season in spring and the Trout in autumn and winter. In May a Trout is in good condition and a Grayling in a bad state.

Grayling enjoy everywhere a very high reputation for their white and firm flesh of excellent flavour. While Trout may sometimes be coarse to eat, the Grayling is invariably delicate. Steamed and served cold with mayonnaise, baked in a paper bag, fried, or plain grilled, they are a dish for epicures.

THE SMELT (Osmerus eperlanus)

Strictly speaking this fish is not a Salmonid, but it is closely related, and bears the "adipose" fin of that family. It has a very slender shape, a large mouth, a *short lateral line* that does not extend beyond ten or twelve scales after the gill-cover. It is silvery in colour, with the back greenish.

The Smelt is a sea fish that enters estuaries to spawn. It is commoner on the eastern and western coasts than on the southern—the Forth, Conway and East Anglian estuaries being the most frequented. It used to ascend the Thames as high up as Richmond, and "John Bickerdyke" stated fifty years ago that the Smelt was plentiful in the Thames and Medway estuaries. Pollution and overfishing have changed matters, unfortunately for the London anglers, who would welcome a chance to fish for such a sporting and tasty quarry.

The Smelt grows to a length of a little over a foot and a weight of 8 to 10 oz. It is mostly caught in nets, but it may be angled, using as bait a shrimp, a worm or a fragment of fish. It is a voracious fish with a very quick digestion that forces it always to be seeking for food, such as small fish, crustacea and worms.

The spawning season lasts from March to May. The fish congregate in shoals in the estuaries, and lay rather large yellow eggs that stick to the bottom on rocks, gravel or weeds. The fry hatch out in a period varying from 8 to 25 days, according, as usual, to the temperature of the water. The young fish spend from four to six months in the estuary, where some of the adult fish also remain for months. The Smelt may live and prosper in brackish or fresh waters.

This fish is particularly good in the autumn and early spring, and may be cooked like Grayling or Trout. It is said that the Smelt smells of cucumber, just as the Grayling is said to smell of thyme or violets. I confess I have failed to detect such delicate scents in these fish, although I am credited with a keen nose. In my opinion, both fish smell of fish, but in an agreeable way.

The true Smelt, with its slim shape, adipose fin and short lateral line, cannot be mistaken for any other fish. Note that the so-called *Sand Smelt* or *Atherine* (*Atherina presbyter*), so common on the South Coast in summer, is not even remotely related to the Smelt. The Sand Smelt has *two* true dorsal fins, the first spiny, the second with rays, and a long silvery band along the body, from head to tail. It is good eating and good sport in spite of its very small size, but not comparable to the true Smelt under either aspect.

20

THE SHADS (*Alosae*—Herring Family)

THE Shads are sea fish of the Herring family that spawn in fresh water like some members of the Salmon family, and that, like them, may take permanent residence there; several large lakes of the Alpine region contain non-migratory Shad.

In the British Isles there are two species, both marine, that enter rivers on the western coasts of Britain and Ireland, mostly the Severn and the Shannon. Some got into Killarney lakes through the Laune, perhaps mistaking Dingle Bay for the mouth of the Shannon; some people believe that the Killarney Shad is a small landlocked variety (*Alosa finta killarnensis*).

Both fish in colour and appearance resemble rather portly and very large Herrings, hence the name "King of the Herrings" given them (as well as to several other species) by fishermen. The distinctive characteristics of both Shads are: *single, soft dorsal fin—no lateral line*—tail deeply forked—*gill-covers with many lines* (such as the Pilchard has)—very small and feeble teeth.

The ALLIS SHAD (*Clupea alosa* or *Alosa alosa*) is the largest species, reaching a maximum weight of 8 lb. and a length of $2\frac{1}{2}$ ft. On the young fish there is a row of longitudinal dark blotches on the upper part of each side of the body, but in the older specimens there may be only one dark spot left, on the shoulder, above the gill opening. There are *from 72 to 86 scales* in a *longitudinal* series from the gills to the tail (there is no lateral line), and *from 21 to 25* in a *vertical* series from the dorsal to the ventral fins.

The TWAITE SHAD (*Clupea* or *Alosa finta* or *fallax*) is commoner but smaller, being seldom heavier than 4 lb. or longer than 20 in. It retains even in the adult stage the row of dark spots found only in the young of the Allis. The scales are smaller and firmer; there are *from 58 to 66* in a *longitudinal* series, and *from 16 to 20* in a *vertical* series of scales.

The most important distinction between the two species is

represented by the gill-rakers. If you lift the gill-cover and examine the first gill-arch you will find that the Allis Shad has a *great number* (from 60 to 120) *of fine gill-rakers*, as long as or longer than the gills, while the Twaite Shad has *from 30 to 45 gill-rakers, rather stiff and short* (shorter than the gills).

Both Shads spawn at night in late spring, between April and June, when they ascend estuaries and rivers. The eggs are small and numerous, and are laid on the bottom of the river. The period of incubation is short, and the fry grow to 4 to 6 in. in their first year of life, spent mostly in fresh or brackish water. From that time onwards they live at sea, returning to the rivers to spawn.

They are occasionally angled at sea when whiffing for Mackerel, or caught in drift nets or seines. A few in the Severn fall victims to a fly-spoon or other small spinning lure. Shads caught before spawning are very good food, with a slight salmon flavour. They may be grilled, baked, steamed or stewed; in any case, when you eat them, you will find in the innumerable bones an additional proof of their being members of the Herring family.

NOTE. Do not mix the *Shad* with the *Scad* or Horse Mackerel (*Caranx trachurus*); that belongs to a different Order and is a strictly marine species.

21

THE PIKE (*Esox lucius*—Family *Esocidae*)
Plate 4

THE Pike is the only British representative of its family, and cannot easily be mistaken for any other fish. Rather elongated in body, it has a broad flattened head, and a very large mouth bristling with sharp teeth which sprout even from its tongue. Its one dorsal fin is placed near its tail, almost directly over the anal fin. Its scales are rather small (i.e. 125 to 130 along the lateral line. It is in colour greenish grey or olive with yellowish marblings, and has a white belly and spotted fins.

It is found practically everywhere in the British Isles, always "a solitary, melancholy and bold fish . . . the tyrant of the rivers, the freshwater wolf, by reason of his bold, greedy, devouring disposition." In warm weather it lingers near the surface, in slow-running water or in the weedy shallows of lakes and ponds; in the colder months it retires to deeper water, but seeks the sunniest reaches. Its coloration makes it well-nigh invisible when half hidden among the rushes and the water lilies, where it lies motionless, ready to pounce like lightning on any unsuspecting prey swimming by. It is much easier to see the Pike in early spring, when there are no weeds to shelter it; you will recognize it at once by its peculiar snout, the fin near the tail and by its immobility. Only its pectorals and gills will move, and then almost imperceptibly. Don't forget that it is quick of sight and hearing, and if alarmed will disappear in a flash.

The Pike grows to a considerable size, especially in anglers' tales. There are many authenticated cases of specimens between 40 and 50 lb. The largest taken by fair angling was caught in Loch Conn in Ireland in 1920, and weighed 53 lb. The English record stands at 37½ lb. (Fordingbridge, 1944); there is also an unofficial record of a 39-lb. 7-oz. Pike angled in the Hampshire Stour in 1909. When Whittlesea Mere was drained in 1851 a very big pike in poor condition was found, weighing 52 lb.; in good condition it would have scaled over 60 lb. A pike caught in Loch Ken is credited with having been 7 ft. long and 72 lb. in weight; its skull is preserved at Kenmore Castle, and its size shows that the fish could have been as large as is claimed. Walton mentions, on Gesner's authority, a pike more than 200 years old found in a German pond, and Ripley ("Believe it or not") adds that the fish was 20 ft. long, 267 years old and weighed 544 lb. Which shows that even fishing tales are not what they were.

The Pike is amazingly voracious, feeding madly at times according to a fairly regular cycle of about eleven days; a great many tales are told about its voracity, some of which have been confirmed. (Over 300 minnows were found inside a fish caught at Hurley, on the Thames.) Its normal diet is composed of fishes, with the addition of ducklings, small swimming birds, rats and voles, frogs and newts. Anglers fish for it with strong tackle (often *too* strong), using as bait small live or dead fish, wooden "plugs" shaped like fishes, or shiny metal spoons, all abundantly garnished with treble hooks; the Pike's mouth is bony and hard, and it is not easy to lodge in it a hook that will hold until the fish is captured.

In the Thames, and in most public waters, it is illegal to catch Pike less than 18 in. long. A fish of this size will weigh approximately 1¾ lb.; at 20 in. about 2½ lb.; at 22 in. about 3¼ lb.; when 2 ft. long about 4¼ lb.; at 26 in. about 5½ lb.; at 28 in. about 7 lb.; when 3 ft. about 15 lb. Naturally these weights are approximate, and vary according to the condition of the fish. Females are usually larger than males.

In many places a Pike not above 5 lb. is called a "jack." A young Pike is called a Pickerel, and as it is usually striped instead of being mottled like the adult, some people are misled into thinking it a different kind of fish.

The Pike is an early spawner, and the eggs are laid between February and May, in large numbers. When first laid they are slightly sticky, and it is possible that in such condition they may be transferred from one stretch of water to another by wildfowl. This would explain the appearance of Pike in ponds and Trout streams where they did not exist before and where they are most unwelcome. The eggs are deposited in shallow water, and the fry remain there only a few days after being hatched, retiring quickly to deeper water. It is not easy therefore to keep the baby fishes under observation. They grow quickly and their appetite is insatiable.

A medium-sized Pike of a few pounds makes very good eating. The best way to prepare it is to stuff it with herbs and bake it in the oven with frequent basting. You will find that old Izaak was right in saying that "this dish of meat is too good for any but anglers, or very honest men," even if you don't follow his very complicated recipe.

CAUTION. When handling a Pike, dead or alive, keep your hands away from its mouth, because those wicked teeth can cause very unpleasant cuts and scratches. If you must remove hooks from its mouth, use a "gag" and a "disgorger" that you can get for a few pence from a tackle shop.

22

THE EEL (*Anguilla anguilla*—Eel family)

IF we hear a "mysterious creature" mentioned, our mind unconsciously evokes the image of a dark, sinuous, heavy-lidded and lightly dressed woman. Possibly because I am not a very active frequenter of cinemas, my mind turns instead to the Eel; it is also sinuous, slippery and dangerous to weaker creatures, but infinitely more mysterious; it has the advantage, not shared by the other kind of "mysterious creatures," of being very useful in the kitchen, though in a passive way (anyone who has skinned an Eel will object to my use of the word "passive"). The mystery of the Eel has puzzled mankind for many centuries, long before Aristotle expressed it first, and it is still not entirely solved. For twenty-five centuries naturalists have formed hypotheses about this fish, displaying an imaginative power usually restricted to the novelist or the poet; read for instance the chapter on the Eel in the *Compleat Angler*.

There is a part of the Eel's life that is not particularly mysterious. We know that in the summer months incredible numbers of minute Eels or *Elvers* appear at the mouths of rivers. They are about 2 in. long, as thick as string, nearly transparent. They swarm upstream in an almost solid mass, wriggling up the weirs, on the wet stones, on the weeds. They spread to all the waters they can reach, even land-locked ponds, wriggling at night in the grass, wet with rain or dew. Some remain in the estuaries, in brackish or salt water, perhaps for life, but usually going sooner or later into fresh water. They prefer muddy or tangled spots, where they can hide during daytime, either buried in the mud or ensconced in cracks or holes, in the roots under the bank or under stones. The young Eels grow slowly; after a year in fresh water they are about 4 in. long, after two about $5\frac{1}{2}$ in., and in the third summer, when a little over 7 in., scales begin to form on the middle of each side. These scales are of a peculiar kind, and have been carefully studied by the Danish biologist Gemzöe, who was able to throw much light on the development of the fish. He found that as the Eel feeds and grows mostly in summer, the little oval scales show growth-rings comparable with those of trees; by counting these rings, and adding the years passed before scale formation began, it is possible to ascertain the age of any particular fish. Thus he showed that when the Eels are about six years old the females begin to grow faster than the males, and that they reach maturity after having spent from six and a half to eight and a half years in fresh water and reached sizes from 14 to 26 in., while the males passed five and a half or six and a half years before maturity, and growing to a length of from 12 to 20 in. A few fish remain for a longer period in fresh water and grow to a much larger size; exceptionally large Eels may be anything between ten and thirty years old.

During this period the Eel eats voraciously anything of an animal nature that it can find and swallow: worms, larvae, fish, offal, fish spawn, water birds, voles and rats, frogs, newts and crustacea. The larger specimens often show an exaggerated development of their jaws and jaw muscles, which has secured for them the names of Frog-mouth, Bulldog, Grig, Broad-nosed or Gorb-eel, and the temporary elevation to the rank of a distinct species. The colour ranges from almost black to sandy, being darkest on the back; the belly is white or yellow; the commonest shade is yellow, whence the name of Yellow Eel given to the fish in their growing, non-migratory dress. During this period the internal difference between the sexes is so small that a dissection and a careful examination are needed to ascertain the point.

Small Congers may be mistaken for Common Eels when found near estuaries; you may distinguish the two species quite easily. The Conger has *large* gill slits that reach the belly; *the dorsal fin begins above the end of the pectorals* (in the Common Eel it begins a long way after).

After spending at least five (males) or six (females) years in fresh water the Eels approach sexual maturity, and their appearance begins to change: their colour becomes almost black on the back and silvery white on the belly, while on the sides there is a bronze stripe; the head becomes more rounded and the snout sharper, the eyes are bigger and more on the side of the head, the pectoral fins longer, pointed and almost black; the digestive system shrinks while the sexual organs develop. At this stage they are called Silver or Sharp-nosed Eels; they feed very little, and during the darkest nights of late summer and autumn they go down to the sea, and are caught in traps, baskets or nets placed mostly in weirs or at the effluence of lakes. Those that reach the sea disappear for ever.

What happens between the departure of the Silver Eels and the arrival of the Elvers has puzzled naturalists until a few years ago, and some points are still obscure. During these last years this part of the wonderful story of the Eel has been often told, but I hope my readers will not object to my giving a brief outline of it. Its discovery is a good instance of the old truism that Science (or knowledge, if you prefer to call it so) knows no boundaries.

In Aristotle's days people knew of a queer little fish, shaped like a willow leaf, almost transparent, with a tiny head; it had no economic importance, and nobody bothered about it. These odd little creatures were first studied and classified under the name of Leptocephali (thin heads) by the Italian naturalist Scopoli in 1777. In 1861 Carus, a German, expressed the opinion that the Leptocephali were larval fishes, and thought they were the larvae of Deal-fish. The American Gill in 1864 believed that *L. morrisii* (first captured by the British William Morris) was the larva of the Conger, and in 1886 the French biologist Delage proved experimentally that this opinion was correct. In 1893 two Italian biologists, Grassi and Calandruccio, by observing a great many speciments of Leptocephali brought to the surface by the powerful whirlpools of the Straits of Messina, were able to reconstruct the gradual development of Leptocephali into elvers.

A great step had been made, but the period between the entry into the sea of the Silver Eels and the appearance of the Leptocephali was as dark as ever. It was believed that the Eels spawned near the coasts, but the Leptocephali were usually found far out at sea, and Günther suggested they were abnormal larvae from eggs carried accidentally to a great distance from land, where their development had been affected by the uncongenial surroundings. This gap in our knowledge has been almost completely filled by the Danish zoologist Johannes Schmidt. Danish investigators had already found that the migrating Silver Eels in the Baltic travelled parallel to the coast in a fixed direction, so much so that unless eel-baskets were set in a certain immutable position no fish were caught. Many Eels were marked, and the direction and speed of their journey had been ascertained: they *all* went out of the Baltic and towards the Atlantic. Schmidt began a systematic search for Eels and Leptocephali, and during several voyages on the Danish research steamer *Thor* he was able to discover that the farther one went towards the West Indies the smaller and more abundant became the Leptocephali of the Eel and of the Conger. The smallest and youngest were found over very deep water about half-way between the Leeward Islands and Bermuda, and this zone must be considered the birth-place of the European Eel (though it is possible that the great depths of the Mediterranean are chosen by some of the Eels living in the countries bordering on it). It is sure that the Eel spawns at a depth not found on the Continental Shelf surrounding our isles; it is also obvious that water over 2,000 fathoms deep is not easy to study, and therefore it is not surprising that we do not know yet the perfectly mature fish, the fertilized egg or the newly born larva. The Eels, once they have spawned, probably die; at all events, none return to the rivers.

The spawning season probably goes from early spring until well into summer. Tiny Leptocephali, about $\frac{1}{3}$ in. long, appear about this time at a depth varying between 100 and 150 fathoms; they feed on microscopical plankton life, and grow rapidly, reaching a length of about 1 in. by the autumn. Then they move to the upper layers of the Western Atlantic. By their second summer of life they are about 2 in., and have shifted to the Central Atlantic. During their third summer they reach the coastal zones of Europe, and are about 3 in., still leaf-shaped and transparent. During the cold months the Leptocephali shrink in size and become round, their blood becomes red: they have turned into Elvers, and ascend the rivers as their parents did in their time.

Eels used to be very abundant in British rivers, and still are in cleaner waters; the Dutch canals and polders supply not only their own but a large percentage of the British market. Most Eels are caught in nets or baskets and in traps set on weirs; others fall to night lines, but only a small number are intentionally angled for. I say *intentionally*, because (especially when the weather is thundery) Eels have a way of gobbling the worm meant for other fish, and turn the cast, the line and themselves into an inextricable tangle, which supplies infinite amusement to the onlookers and helpless exasperation to the unfortunate angler. If you go for Eels use tough tackle and large hooks with a long shank; then you'll be able to handle the fish quickly and resolutely, grasping it with a piece of sackcloth smeared with sand, that gives you a good hold on this slippery customer; you may also hold it between your middle finger and the back of the other fingers.

There are old records of Eels weighing 20, 23 and 27 lb., but I believe the heaviest caught in recent times was one of 16½ lb., netted in 1926 in the Whitadder. The largest angled by rod and line (near Bristol in 1922) weighed 8½ lb.

To skin an Eel nail the head to a board, cut the skin just behind the pectoral fins, grab it firmly with a piece of coarse cloth, and pull it off like a glove; the skin is very tough and won't tear.

The Eel is not only one of the tastiest but also one of the most nutritious of fishes, its average calorie value being 799 per pound, according to Plimmer, compared with the 276 of Cod and the 272 of Trout. It may be cooked in many ways, but friend Ingoldsby reminds us that:

"... if you chance to be partial to eels,
Then—crede experto—trust one who has tried—
Have them spitch-cock'd or stewed—they're too oily when fried."

Spitch-cocked (Grilled) Eel. Split the skinned eel lengthwise in two halves, remove the backbone and grill; when half cooked, sprinkle with pepper and salt and a pinch of mixed herbs; broil till brown and serve hot with a squeeze of lemon or mustard sauce. Do not add oil or fat.

Stewed Eel à la Florentine. Slice a large onion (and a clove of garlic, if you like it) and fry till golden brown in very little oil or fat. Put in a pound of eel cut into chunks 2 in. long, and fry quickly (turning to prevent sticking) till it begins to get brown. Season, add a pinch of herbs and cover with good red wine. If you have any dried mushrooms or fresh ones (the stalks will do, cut into slices) or chillies, or peppers, put them in, and boil for about a quarter of an hour till almost cooked. Remove the chunks of fish and thicken the gravy with some tomato purée (lacking this, use cornflour), boiling for a few minutes. Put the fish back into the gravy (if you leave it in the whole time you risk "catching") and simmer for another five or ten minutes. Serve hot.

Jellied Eels. This famous Cockney delicacy is prepared according to many different recipes. Here is one of them: Cut the fish in chunks, and put into a saucepan with half its weight of vegetables (onion, carrots, celery, with a few bay leaves, parsley, sage, etc.), add the smallest amount of water to cover the mixture, season and bring slowly to the boil under a small flame. Keep simmering gently for at least an hour (more if the fish is thick) remove the pieces of eel to a deep jar or pot, boil off about a quarter of the stock, strain through butter muslin, add a small glass of white wine and pour over the fish. When cold this stock will set as a jelly.

Marinated or Pickled Eels. In the lagoons of Comacchio, Italy, enormous quantities of eels are captured and sold either fresh or "marinated." The pickling is done as follows, and may be applied to other kinds of fish. Cut the eels in pieces about 2 in. long, grill them (or roast on a spit) till golden. In the meantime bring *quickly* to the boil some *strong* vinegar, to which are added salt, peppercorns, sultanas, a little treacle, sliced onion and chillies, a few cloves of garlic cut into halves, bay, sage and rosemary leaves to taste; boil for a couple of minutes, drop the cooked fish into the pickle, bring again to the boil and pour everything in large earthen jars, seal, and use cold with some of the pickle. These pickled eels are extensively sold in barrels, and enjoy a deserved reputation as a tasty *hors-d'oeuvre*.

23

THE CARP FAMILY (*Cyprinidae*)

GENERAL CHARACTERISTICS. *One* dorsal fin—ventral fins on the belly—pectoral fins rather low—well-developed anal and caudal fins—*lateral line present* (often incomplete in Minnow)—*mouth toothless* (the teeth are in the throat, on the lower bones of the gullet)—spawning season: spring and early summer, when the males acquire special coloration and small warts on head—

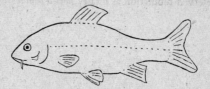

Fig. 7—A Typical Cyprinid

Dorsal fin on middle of back—soft fins—lateral line—mouth often with barbels, but toothless—ventral fins abdominal (on belly).

some mostly vegetarian, others also eat small fishes, insects and worms—usually move in shoals or small groups—form hybrids, which will be described at the end of this chapter.

For identification purposes we may divide them into several groups, according to their mode of life or external peculiarities:

With barbels: Carp, Barbel, Tench, Gudgeon.

With a long dorsal fin: Carp, Crucian Carp, Goldfish.

Always of small size: Minnow, Gudgeon, Bleak.

Prefer still water (ponds, lakes, backwaters): All Carps, Breams, Rudd, Tench (Roach).

In sunny weather prefer surface: Bleak, Rudd, Dace, Chub, Roach.

Keep to the bottom: Gudgeon, Tench, Barbel, Bream (Carps).

More or less silvery: Chub, Dace, Roach, Rudd, Silver Bream, Bleak.

Body more or less deep: Carps, Roach, Rudd, Breams.

Large scales: Carps, Chub, Roach, Rudd, Breams.

Or, more scientifically, as follows:

I. With a *long dorsal* fin, anal short: (1) four small barbels, dorsal
fin concave—Carp; (2) no barbels, dorsal fin convex—
Crucian Carp and Goldfish.

II. With *short* dorsal fin, anal short: (A) with barbels: (*a*) four
barbels—Barbel; (*b*) two barbels: (1) rounded fins, very
small scales—Tench; (2) straight fins, largish scales, mouth
under snout—Gudgeon. (B) without barbels: (*a*) small
scales, small size—Minnow; (*b*) large scales, body narrow:
(1) anal fin rounded (convex)—Chub; (2) anal fin dented
(concave)—Dace; (*c*) large scales, body fairly deep:
(1) upper lip longest—Roach; (2) lower lip longest—
Rudd.

III. With short dorsal fin, *anal long*: (*a*) body deep: (1) from 23
to 29 rays in anal fin—Bronze Bream; (2) from 19 to 24
rays in anal fin—Silver Bream; (*b*) body slim—Bleak.

THE CARP (*Cyprinus carpio*)

The Carp is the pond fish *par excellence*; it prospers in small
muddy moats, ditches and stagnant pools where most fishes
would die in a short time. It prospers, and grows to a large size
and a ripe old age because, any embittered angler will tell you,
a large Carp is purely and simply not to be caught. For once,
you may believe the stories you will hear about the cunning of
the Carp. Walton called it " a stately, a good and a very subtle
fish—hard to be caught—the river-fox for cunning"; this
description is complete and exact even to-day. Many ponds
have been stocked with Carp, and many are overstocked, so that
you will find them full of fingerlings that have no chance to grow
because the food supply is too small for their numbers. Any
boy with a small hook can catch Carp then, and start a little
aquarium of his own. These little Carp are quite pretty, very
hardy, and become very tame; they can take with advantage the

place of Goldfish. In well-balanced ponds Carp will not be numerous, but they will be of a much larger size; on a sunny summer day you can observe them easily, if you keep quiet. They will rise to the surface and bask in the sunshine, moving in a stately way here and there, nibbling gently under the water-lily leaves, and sometimes taking a gulp of air with a loud smacking noise. If you throw them bits of bread it will be willingly accepted. If it is sweet-cake they will feast on it. Try to conceal a hook and line in the same bait, and they will ignore it with a scornful ostentation that you will find galling; and if the fish will continue rudely to smack their thick lips all over the pond, your irritation will become exasperation. Or your bait will be gently seized with the very skin of the lips, and carried about; if you strike, the fish will not be hooked, and even if you do not strike, the bait will most probably be dropped as soon as the Carp suspects anything—that is, very soon. Nor is it much easier to net these fish in large stretches of water, because they will find ways to wriggle into the mud and avoid the meshes. Carp have a varied diet that enables them to find food almost anywhere. They eat vegetable matter from bread to the young leaves of water plants, and shrimps, worms, grubs and larvae of insects, as well as mouthfuls of mud which they spit out after some time; occasionally they will even take insects floating on the pond (but *don't* try fly-fishing). In winter Carp cease feeding, withdraw to deep holes and bury themselves in mud, where they remain in a torpid state till the spring.

The body of the Carp is usually fairly deep and thick, especially if food is plentiful; the back is dark olive brown, fading to bronze on the sides and to pale yellow on the belly. The scales are large, numbering *from 34 to 40 along the lateral line; the dorsal fin is long and with a concave edge* (from 17 to 22 soft branched rays, the third being stiff and saw-edged); the ventral fins often orange or pale pink; *tail fin well forked*; from 5 *to 7 scales* from the beginning of the dorsal fin to the lateral line; *anal fin short*, with a first stiff, rough ray (7 to 8 rays); *four barbels*, two pale and small sprouting from upper lip and two longer ones (orange or red) from the corners of the mouth.

IDENTIFICATION. The Common Carp may be mistaken for the *Crucian Carp*, and for the *Common* or *Bronze Bream*, or for *Goldfish* that have lost their gilt. None of these three fishes has barbels, as the Carp has. The Carp has a well-forked tail, unlike the Crucian Carp and the Goldfish; the Carp has a dorsal fin which is concave, with the longest rays at its beginning; the Crucian Carp has a rounded, convex dorsal, with the highest rays in the middle. The number of scales along the lateral line is from 34 to 40 in the Carp, 28 to 35 in the Crucian Carp and 25 to 30 in the Goldfish.

The Bream is flatter and deeper than the Carp, and unlike the Carp it has a *short* dorsal fin and a *long* anal fin.

Carp spawn in late spring and early summer; the males have then small white warts on the sides of their heads; the fish frequent weedy shallows, where they splash noisily about, stirring the mud from the bottom. Often two or three males may be seen following a female; the eggs laid are very numerous, a large female dropping several hundreds of thousands. The fry hatch quickly and grow rapidly if conditions are favourable.

As we said, Carp grow to a large size; the largest British-angled fish weighed 26 lb., and was caught in 1930 in a private reservoir near Ilkeston. Bigger fish have been taken on the Continent, and one of 41½ lb. was hooked at Florida Lake, Transvaal. Carp over 15 lb. are to be considered among the choicest trophies of any angler. The minimum legal size is generally 12 in., when the fish would average 1 lb. 2 oz.; when 15 in. about 2¼ lb.; when 18 in. about 4 lb.

The Carp keeps alive out of water for a long time, especially if packed in wet moss wrapped in a wet cloth. It can then be easily transported and put into glass bowls if small or into ponds if large.

Carp are easily reared, and on the Continent are the object of large-scale cultivation both for ornament and culinary use. Breeders have managed to obtain freak forms, such as the

"Leather Carp," without scales, or the "Mirror Carp," with only one or two rows of exceptionally large and shiny scales. In several countries on the Continent the Carp enjoys the reputation of being very tasty. Personally, having eaten Carp in three different countries, I consider it rather poor fare; only when the muddy tang has been covered by a generous supply of various condiments does the fish begin to be eatable. Here is a good recipe that may be used for other fish of the Carp family.

Chop finely a large onion, a stick of celery and a carrot; fry them in oil or margarine. When the onion begins to brown add a handful of parsley, also finely chopped, and, if possible, two or three peeled tomatoes cut in small pieces. Clean the fish and stuff it with finely minced onion and herbs mixed with dripping. Place the fish in the gravy, add enough *dry* red or white wine to cover it, and simmer slowly until cooked. People who object to the taste of wine may increase the number of tomatoes, or use tomato purée dissolved in water, adding a spoonful of vinegar.

THE CRUCIAN CARP (*Carassius carassius*)
Plate 5

This Carp is not so widespread as the Common species, and is found in abundance only in Eastern and South-eastern England. Only occasionally does it occur in ponds in other districts, where it has been artificially introduced. Its habits and mode of life are practically those of the Common Carp; if anything, it is even more tenacious of life and more easy-going. It rivals the Tench in being able to thrive in the muddiest and foulest puddles and ditches, and gives little or no trouble to the aquarist who "cannot be bothered."

Another variety of a slightly slimmer build and with a more forked tail, called *Prussian Carp*, is found more often in garden ponds than in natural surroundings. Its fundamental characteristics are those of the Crucian Carp, which are: colour, olive brown fading to brassy on the belly; *no barbels*, rounded back, with a long, *rounded and convex dorsal fin*, tail slightly *forked, with rather rounded flukes*, lateral line with large scales (from 28 to 35), from $6\frac{1}{2}$ to 9 scales in a line from the beginning of the dorsal fin to the lateral line; the saw-edged spine in the dorsal and anal fins is weaker than in the Carp or Goldfish.

The Crucian Carp does not reach the size of the Common Carp; it is usually small, and fish over a foot in length are seldom caught. Exceptionally it may reach a weight of almost 7 lb. The largest specimen angled in Britain (Godalming, 1938) weighed 4 lb. 11 oz.

IDENTIFICATION. It may be confused, especially when very small, with the *Common Carp*, the *Goldfish* and the *Bream*. Keep in mind that the dorsal fin is long and rounded in the Crucian Carp, which has no barbels, and a short anal fin; the number of scales along the lateral line (28 to 35) will help to distinguish it from dull-coloured Goldfish.

THE GOLDFISH (*Carassius auratus*)

This species is of recent importation into Britain, where it has been introduced as an ornament of aquaria and ponds. As such, it is to be found in many localities, and it is possible that it may spread to other waters. Therefore, it may be useful to know how to identify this species, because the Goldfish easily loses its gilt appearance when in the wild state (as has happened in Madagascar, where it was introduced with disconcerting results).

When this happens, the Goldfish assumes the greenish-brown colouring of the Crucian Carp, from which it can be distinguished by the dorsal fin, which is *long*, with a *strong saw-edged spine* at its beginning and a practically *straight margin*. The *scales* on the lateral line number *from 25 to 30* (against the 28 to 35 of the Crucian Carp), and those between the beginning of the dorsal fin and the lateral line *from 5 to* $6\frac{1}{2}$ (against $6\frac{1}{2}$ to 9 in the Crucian).

The ornamental varieties of other species, such as the Golden Tench, the Golden Carp and Golden Orfe, and maybe even a particularly golden Rudd, may be mistaken at first sight for a

Goldfish in its golden livery. Both the Golden Carp and Tench have *barbels*, absent in the Goldfish; these two species conform exactly with their non-golden brethren in everything except colour. The Rudd and the Orfe have a *short* dorsal fin.

The Goldfish is not a fish on the anglers' list, so that there are no records of maximum weights. In some old fishponds, such as those in Hampton Court or Woburn Abbey, huge Goldfish may be seen, but never caught, measured and weighed. I have seen some that I estimated to be between 1½ and 2 ft. long, and weighing probably between 3 and 5 lb., a size that may seem incredible to anybody familiar only with glass-bowl specimens, but it is also vouched for by an authority as great as Dr. Tate Regan.

Goldfish spawn easily in ponds, and in China, Japan and Italy they are bred in great quantities for ornamental purposes.

I have never met anyone who has eaten Goldfish, and I am therefore compelled to go back as far as 1797 for an opinion on the subject; it was given by Sir John Hawkins in his edition of the *Compleat Angler*. He states that Goldfish "though costly, are but coarse food."

THE BARBEL (*Barbus barbus*)

The Barbel has a strictly local distribution. It is found only in a few rivers of Eastern England, affluents of the prehistoric Rhine (which used to reach farther north than the mouth of the present-day Humber). It inhabits the Thames and some of its tributaries (as the Lea and the Kennet), the Hampshire Avon, the Trent, the Yorkshire Ouse and parts of their basins. Even in these rivers the fish is not to be found everywhere. It favours the swift gravelled streams near weirs, deep and shallow alike, or the deep and fast currents between the buttresses of bridges. In such waters shoals of Barbel swim powerfully against the rapid flow, hugging the bottom with their flat bellies and rooting in the gravel with their leathery snouts, exploring for their food with the barbels (little beards) that have given them their name. It is possible occasionally, in shallow water, especially during the summer months, to see them splashing on the surface or to catch glimpses of their silvery underparts as they roll over on the gravel. Your only chance otherwise of seeing the fish is to catch one—not an easy job.

Though its taste in food is catholic, including worms, crustacea, insects and their larvae, small fishes and vegetable matter—to which may be added the lumps of cheese paste and the greaves contributed by hopeful anglers—the Barbel is a wary creature and only a generous ground-baiting of the neighbourhood will induce it to nibble at the prepared lures. It feeds mostly after dark, and you cannot "fish too early or too late" for it. Even when hooked it is far from being yours, for it is one of the strongest fighters of our rivers, and will do its best to break your line by sheer force, by tangling it in submerged snags or, as a last resort, by rubbing it on the bottom. The hemp-seed angler in quest of Roach, unless he is an expert and a lucky one withal, is often left lamenting his broken gossamer tackle, when he has the doubtful luck of hooking a Barbel, a big one that "gets away." Barbel can easily be "big," because they grow to a length of 3 ft. and a weight of over 15 lb. (sometimes even more in the great rivers of the Continent). The biggest Barbel angled weighed 16 lb. and was caught in the Lea in 1880; fish over 10 lb. are caught only seldom nowadays, and recent records are not over 14 lb. 6 oz.

The distinguishing characteristics of the Barbel are: body long and slim, slightly flattened below; colour varying from dark greenish to olive, fading on the sides and becoming white on the belly; *mouth crescent-shaped, well below the snout*, with thick lips and *four barbels*; eye rather small and high up. The dorsal fin has a strong saw-edged spine, and the other fins are tinged with red; scales rather small, *numbering from 52 to 70 along the lateral line*; occasionally small brownish spots may be present on the back, sides and on the dorsal fin.

Barbel spawn in May or June, when the males are adorned with the usual small warts of the Carp tribe; the eggs are numerous, small and of a yellow colour, laid on gravel.

Very small Barbel may be confused with Gudgeon or Loaches. In these three fishes spots are numerous on the body and on the dorsal and tail fins. None of them has a spine in the dorsal fin. They are best differentiated by the barbels, of which the Gudgeon has *two* and the Loaches *six*, compared with the Barbel's *four*. (In small specimens the barbels are not too obvious, and a little care will be necessary.)

The minimum legal size is usually 16 in., when the fish weighs about $1\frac{1}{2}$ lb.

The flesh of the Barbel, though firm and of good appearance, is of poor quality, and can be made tolerable only by rich cooking with abundant condiments, such as suggested for the Carp.

CAUTION. The spawn and roes of the Barbel, especially in the spawning season or near it, are certainly unwholesome and possibly poisonous; they *must* be removed from the fish before cooking it, particularly if the fish is caught in summer.

THE TENCH (*Tinca tinca*)
Plate 6

The same kind of water that holds Carp is also beloved of the Tench, which is probably the most sluggish of our freshwater fishes. Its power of making the best of the worst waters allows it to prosper in weedy and muddy puddles where even a Crucian Carp would feel uncomfortable. It moves about only by night, and in daytime it keeps to the bottom, in the mud or the weeds; only very exceptionally, in calm and sunny summer days, it may approach the surface, and there lie motionless under the flags or water-lilies. If disturbed or alarmed, it will immediately dive to the bottom and bury itself in the mud, its favourite element. If this happens in shallow water, you may easily catch the fish with your hand, by groping cautiously in the mud until you have seized your Tench firmly yet gently. Most probably the fish will not even wriggle. It is very tenacious of life, and will survive a long period spent in the open air. You may keep your prey in a bowl or garden pond, and it will live there easily, giving little trouble, but also little satisfaction, on account of its laziness and fondness for a muddy bottom.

The Tench is distributed irregularly over the British Isles up to Central Scotland. In many cases the fish has been artificially introduced into ponds, drains and clay pits.

The general impression given by the Tench is that of roundness. The body is rather stout, with a rounded back; *all the fins are rounded*, even the *lobes of the tail*. The snout is short and round, with an oblique mouth at its end, and *a small barbel on either side near the corner*. The colour varies from a deep olive to blackish brown; an ornamental variety is golden. The *body is very slimy*, and in the old days many stories were told of the curative powers of this slime for other fishes. The *eye is small and red*. The *scales are very small and numerous* (from 90 to 120 along the lateral line). The smallness of the scales and the presence of two barbels distinguish the Tench from any other fish of its family.

The food of this fish consists of weeds, mud, worms, insects and their larvae, and small shellfish, snails being naturally preferred as being even slower than their captors. Tench are far more easily caught than Carp. The angler should bait with a small worm, paste or a snail, fish in the evening, have plenty of patience, and wait until the fish has decided to take the bait in its mouth. The Tench may be quite good eating, its flavour owing nothing to the quality of its native waters. The recipe for Carp is excellent for cooking Tench.

Even in spawning the Tench is slow, and is probably the latest spawner of our Cyprinids, laying its small and numerous eggs in June. Like other members of the same family, it deposits its eggs in shallow water, on weeds, where they hatch in a few days. The young fish develop fairly quickly, and in favourable surroundings may reach $\frac{1}{4}$ lb. in about a year. In Britain Tench grow to about

8 lb.; the largest caught by fair angling weighed 7 lb. (one of this size was landed at Weston-super-Mare in 1882 and one near Norwich in 1933).

The minimum legal size is usually 8 in. or 10 in., with corresponding weights of 6 and 10 oz.; at 12 in. the weight is a little over 1 lb., and at 15 in. about 2 lb.

THE GUDGEON (*Gobio gobio*)

Plate 7

The Gudgeon looks like a miniature Barbel, being similar in shape, and, like its bigger brother, lives always on the bottom of of the stream, preferably on gravel. You may sometimes see a Barbel splash on the surface, but not Gudgeon, except when spawning in the shallows in the months of April and May. You may see instead shoals of Gudgeon grubbing with their snouts on the gravel or in the sand, stirring up the bottom in search of small insect larvae, worms, little crustacea and vegetable substances. The Gudgeon is not so circumscribed in his surroundings as is the Barbel, and may dwell in quiet, small streams, lakes and even muddy ponds. In spite of these accommodating tastes, it is not found everywhere. While very common in most parts of the British Isles, it is not found in Scotland, the Lake District, Cornwall and parts of Wales. It is a hardy little fish, and it will prosper in garden ponds, staying, of course, on the bottom.

The Gudgeon has a slim body, rather flattened underneath; the colour varies a great deal, being grey or brown, with silvery or golden tints on the sides broken by blue-black spots arranged in a line of irregular squares; the dorsal and caudal fins are speckled with little brown or grey spots; the *tail is forked*; it carries *two barbels* at the corners of a *crescent-shaped mouth well below the snout*; the eye is proportionately larger than that of the Barbel, and rather high on the head; *the scales are rather large, from 39 to 45 along the lateral line*; the dorsal fin has from six to eight soft rays and *no spine*.

Gudgeon may be mistaken for very small *Barbel*, *Loaches* and

Minnows. It has only *two* barbels, unlike the Barbel (*four*) and the Loaches (six); the Minnow has *no* barbels. The Gudgeon has large scales, unlike all the other four fishes. The Loaches have a rounded tail and the Gudgeon's is forked.

The Gudgeon is a small species, and a specimen 8 in. long is a giant. The biggest Gudgeon that has ever been caught by angling weighed 4¼ oz., but Mr. Marshall Hardy reports that, in emptying the reservoir of Messrs. Clay & Co. at Bungay, Gudgeon weighing about half a pound were found.

The eggs are small, sticky and transparent, with a pale blue tinge; spawning takes place at intervals, and the males have the usual ornamental warts of the tribe.

This little fish is easily caught with a small hook baited either with bread or, even better, with small worms or maggots. Stirring the bottom with a rake, a stick or an oar will bring the fish on the feed almost immediately, if they are present. In spite of its size, it struggles valiantly on light tackle. Unlike most members of its family it is very dainty eating, so much so that this quality is the first remembered about it by Walton. Fried in breadcrumbs, it will make you regret its diminutive size.

THE MINNOW (*Phoxinus phoxinus*)
Plate 8

There is a widespread idea, dearly beloved of mothers of boys, that "minnow" and "tiddler" are interchangeable terms, equally apt to describe any fry or tiny fish that their offspring bring home in jam-jars. I hope it will give my young readers some satisfaction to be able to enlighten their elders by a demonstration that the Minnow and the Stickleback are distinct species. I hope also that they will try to pick out the different species from any fry they may capture, although this is a very difficult job.

The Minnow is a very small fish, seldom exceeding 4 in. in length; very exceptionally it reaches 6 or 7 in. It is found practically everywhere in the British Isles except in the North

Highlands and in some counties of the West of Ireland. It lives in any river, lake, pond or stream where the bottom is sandy or gravelly and the water clean. There shoals of Minnow may be seen moving about in processions, usually on the border between the shallows and deeper water. If alarmed by the onlooker they will dart away, but their inquisitiveness will soon get the upper hand and they will return to explore their former grounds, being specially attracted by the presence of anything unusual. Curiosity kills more Minnows than cats, and glass or celluloid traps are used to catch them (to serve as bait for bigger fish).

The Minnow has a *spindle-shaped body*, with irregular dark bars or scattered dark spots marking a silvery-grey background; the back is dark green or brown, bordered on the sides with a golden stripe; the head is rounded, with a *short, round snout*; the *scales are very small* (so much that Walton thought the Minnow scaleless), from 80 to over 100; lateral line often incomplete.

The Minnow may be mistaken for the *Gudgeon* and the *Loaches*, which are also small and dappled. It should be singled out at once by its lack of barbels, present in the other three species. It can be distinguished from small specimens of other species on account of its dappled sides and golden band, unlike the other young Carps, which are uniformly silvery.

The Minnow spawns in May and June, when the males, besides the usual family tubercles, assume a scarlet colour on their belly (similar to that of the Stickleback in the same season); the eggs are numerous and very small, and stick to the gravel in the shallows, where the fish migrate to spawn.

The Minnow feeds on minute animals such as mosquito larvae, small worms and the eggs of fishes, as well as on vegetable matter. It is quite hardy and will live in ponds, provided that they are not muddy, and even in large tanks. It is lively and becomes very tame in a short time.

The Minnow is used mostly as bait for Perch, Trout and Pike. Its small size makes it despised by our cooks, quite wrongly. Walton says that "for excellency of meat it may be compared to any fish of greatest value," and advises his pupils to cut their heads off and fry them with the flowers of cowslips and primroses. More simply, they can be fried as Whitebait, as is done on the Continent.

THE DACE (*Leuciscus leuciscus*)

Plate 9

This fish used to be (and in places still is) called Dare or Dart. The name Dace originally meant the same thing, and arises from the first impression this lively fish gives to the onlooker—that of sudden, quick movement. If you observe it in summer you will see it dashing gracefully here and there in the clear streams it prefers, now leaping at flies on the surface and now diving at some small creature in the gravel, its silvery sides glittering all the time. The Dace is the slenderest and sprightliest member of the Carp family, and it is also a gamesome fish for the angler, who can snare it with a variety of methods, from the bottom with small worms or maggots, and from the top with the fly. The trout fly-fisherman is liable to think that his skill has left him when he tries to hook Dace; he will soon discover, to his relief and at the same time annoyance, that the Dace is quicker than the fastest Trout, and is therefore much more difficult to hook when it rises. He need not be ashamed if he misses three fish out of four, and he may be proud if he hooks one out of three.

The Dace is common in most English and Welsh rivers and streams, but is not found in Scotland or in Ireland (except in the Blackwater River). In summer it may appear almost anywhere —in the fast shallows where Barbel lie, in the weedy "runs" preferred by Roach, or darting at flies on the surface; in the autumn and winter it withdraws to deeper water and keeps to the bottom.

The Dace has a slim body, with a dark back (ranging from brownish to bluish green) grading to silver on the sides and the belly; *the dorsal fin is hollowed out or concave, with 7 or 8 branched rays; the anal fin is also concave, pinkish, with 7 to 9 branched rays;*

F.—6

the ventral fins are yellowish or very pale pink; the scales are of medium size and number from 47 *to* 54 *along the lateral line*.

The Dace may easily (too often and too easily) be mistaken for small *Chub* and small slender *Roach*. You may distinguish it from the Chub by its concave dorsal and anal fins (convex or rounded and redder in the Chub), smaller scales and head. The Roach has concave fins, but they are redder, and the rays in the dorsal and anal fins are more numerous (from 9 to 11 or 12); its scales are also slightly larger and there are fewer than 47.

A quarter-pound Dace is considered a nice fish, and a half-pounder something to tell friends about; a pounder may get you a prize from your newspaper if it caters for anglers. The largest British Dace angled was 1 lb. 8 oz. 5 dr. in weight and was caught in 1932 in a tributary of the Hampshire Avon; good rivers for Dace are the Kennet and the Hampshire Avon.

The Dace spawns in weedy shallows in April and May, and the males have the usual family tubercles on their heads; the eggs are small and develop quickly.

It is a pity that the Dace has a lot of small forked bones, because it is a much better fish for the table than most members of its family. You may cook it as you would Trout; fried or steamed with parsley sauce it is delicious; the fresher it is the better.

THE GOLDEN ORFE (*Leuciscus idus*)

The Orfe or Ide is a Continental fish closely resembling the Dace. A golden variety has been for a long time a great favourite of aquarists, and has been introduced into many ponds. It plays in the upper layers of the water in the fashion of a Dace or Bleak, rising to flies and gnats with great liveliness.

It is slim, with a *short dorsal fin*; the colour is golden with a pink tinge, fading to pinky silver on the belly. In shape, size and behaviour it is like the Dace.

It may be mistaken at first glance for Rudd, Goldfish or golden varieties of Carp and Tench. These last two species have barbels on their mouths; the Rudd has a much wider body and lacks the pink tinge; the Goldfish has a long dorsal fin.

If you have a good garden pool, I strongly recommend stocking it with Golden Orfe; the fish is entertaining, and you may be sure that no mosquitoes will breed there.

THE CHUB (*Leuciscus cephalus*)
(*Loggerhead, Skelly, Chavender*)

This fish looks very much like a bulkier and chubbier edition of the Dace, and when small is very often confused with it. It differs in habits (and tastes differently), but it remains an interesting fish, and one of the most easily observable, provided care is taken.

Dorsal and anal fin of Chub

Dorsal and anal fin of Dace and Roach
Fig. 8

In summer it loves to float lazily near the surface of quiet streams and lakes, under the shadow of bushes and trees, hoping for any windfalls that may drop to fill its voracious stomach. The Chub's diet is very varied: beetles, spiders, grasshoppers, caterpillars, worms, cherries, elderberries, small frogs and fishes, bread, seeds; all are welcome so long as no danger is visible. But any shadow or abrupt movement will cause the Chub to disappear like a ghost, sinking into deep water where its dark greenish back will melt into the bottom and the weeds. Remember that the Chub is "the fearfullest of fishes," and approach its haunts very stealthily, facing the sun, so that no shadow will be projected to give the alarm. When the weather gets colder the Chub resorts to deeper water, still preferring places where tree roots, sunken bushes and occasional eddies and deep holes afford good prospects of food coupled with abundant refuge. The Chub prefers at all times running water and a sandy or gravelly bottom with patches of weed; ponds where there is no current at all are not to its liking.

The Chub is found all over Britain except in Northern Scotland, Western Wales, Cornwall and part of Devon; it is not found in Ireland.

Characteristics. Body rounded and fairly slim, with silvery sides, and a dark-green or brownish-green back—*dorsal fin rounded, convex*—ventral and anal fins red, *anal fin rounded, convex*—*tail fin often with a blackish edge*—*scales large, numbering from 42 to 49 along the lateral line*—in summer large Chub have often a yellow tinge over the silver of their sides—the head is rather large and massive (chubby).

The Chub may *easily* be confused, when small, with *Dace* and slim *Roach*. Bear in mind that the Chub has *dorsal and anal fins curved outwards* (convex), while Dace and Roach have the *same fins curved inwards or dented* (concave); the anglers' tag: " Curved Chub and Dented Dace" will help you to remember the fact.

The Chub grows to a good size; the minimum legal size is usually 12 or 14 in., equivalent to weights of about ¾ or 1¼ lb. The largest caught by hook and line in Britain (1913) weighed 8¼ lb., and it came from the Hampshire Avon, a river well known for the large size of its fish, especially Chub. Their average size varies a great deal from one river to another, the normal fish of one being a giant in another. Chub angling is very varied, and the fish very sporting; this (rather than the edible qualities of the fish which, even if cooked with great care and skill, remains rather poor stuff) explains the long chapters dedicated to its pursuit in angling books (to which I must refer the reader if he intends taking up this branch of angling). The recipes for Carp and general fish ought to be followed; if you try to fry or, even worse, boil the Chub, you will have to pass the dish to your cat.

THE ROACH (*Rutilus* [*Leuciscus*] *rutilus*)
Plate 10

Among freshwater fishermen the Roach is probably the most popular of all fish. At week-ends, in normal times, tens of thousands of "coarse" anglers are busy on its track. Roach fishing has even invented a special kind of rod, the roach pole, a great favourite in London, "where I think there be the best Roach anglers."

The Roach is found in Ireland only in the Blackwater River; the Rudd, which closely resembles it, has usurped its name in that country. This fish is not known in Northern Scotland, and in Devon and Cornwall is found only locally. Elsewhere it is common enough. It is fond of quiet water, and prefers ponds, lakes, canals and the quiet reaches of the rivers. Its figure is not adapted for struggling against fast-flowing water. It is not readily seen, because it lives usually near the bottom, in "runs" between weed banks. In the hot and sunny days of summer it will occasionally rise to the top and take flies; it can then be recognized by its deep shape. It strays into estuaries, and prospers in tidal water, becoming fat and vigorous.

The body of the Roach varies a good deal; as a rule, it is fairly deep, but in some still ponds with good food it becomes so deep as almost to rival the Bream. Where the current is fast or food scanty, Roach may be almost as slim as Dace. Therefore depth of body alone is insufficient to identify the fish. The back is dark green, or blue, or brown, the sides and belly silvery, with rather large scales (*from* 40 *to* 46 along the lateral line). The mouth is small, almost at the end of the snout, *with a projecting upper lip. All fins are more or less tinged with red; the anal is bright red, concave and short; the dorsal fin begins practically above the base of the ventral fins.*

Roach spawn in the late spring, when large shoals gather at suitable places to lay their eggs on the bottom. The eggs are very numerous, transparent and of a very pale green colour. The fry is hatched in 10 or 12 days, and keeps to the shallows for the rest of the year. After spawning, the fish are in poor condition, slimy and rough at the same time. They withdraw for some time into the weeds, feeding on silkweed, worms, crustacea and other small creatures. Later on they take to deeper water, over gravelly swims by the side of banks of rushes and water-lilies; they also frequent quiet eddies near weirs or off the stream, and the slow-flowing currents under bushes or willows. They swim slowly in small shoals, ready to shelter in the weeds if a Pike appears on the scene. Bank and punt anglers fish patiently for them, using small worms, bread paste and crust, hemp-seed, maggots, boiled wheat and barley. Walton calls Roach "water sheep for their simplicity." Since his days Roach must have acquired an insight into the ways of anglers, because (except in some overpopulated ponds or private waters) they have become very crafty and suspicious, and the catching of good Roach in clear water or well-fished rivers requires the very finest tackle and a great deal of skill, patience and untiring attention. The fish is very sporting, so it is not surprising that it is such a favourite among the countless anglers who cannot afford Trout. Its fault is that its flesh is full of small forked bones, often insipid and even muddy. Still, a good Roach from a gravelly river, freshly caught and properly cooked, is not to be despised.

In most districts it is illegal to kill Roach below 8 in. long (weight between 3 and 4 oz.). When 9 in. a Roach is about $\frac{1}{2}$ lb. and at 10 in. about 13 oz. A pounder is $10\frac{1}{2}$ in. long; when a foot long it will scale $1\frac{1}{4}$ lb. and $1\frac{1}{2}$ lb. at 13 in. Specimens above 14 in. are to be sent to the taxidermist and preserved in a glass case as a rarity. The largest rod-caught Roach on record (1938) weighed 3 lb. 14 oz., but fish above 3 lb. are extremely rare; even fish above 2 lb. are uncommon in most waters, and in many places Roach above 1 lb. are considered a good catch.

IDENTIFICATION. *Rudd* are easily mistaken for Roach; *Dace* and *Silver Bream* less easily. To make certain of the distinction, remember that the mouth of the Roach is slightly *below* the snout, so that the *upper* lip protrudes a little; that the dorsal fin begins almost exactly *above* the root of the ventral fins; and that the Roach is silvery. The Rudd, on the other hand, often has a

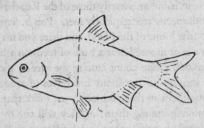

Fig. 9—Shape and position of fins in Roach

golden tinge, fading after death; its mouth is *above* the snout, and it is the *lower* lip that projects; the dorsal fin is nearer to the tail, practically *midway* above the ventral and anal fins.

The Roach differs from the Dace in being deeper, in having a *dorsal fin with 9 to 11 branched rays* (that of the Dace has only 7 or 8), and in having *40 to 46 large scales along the lateral line* (where the Dace has 47 to 54 smaller scales).

It can be distinguished from the Silver Bream by its *short* anal fin (the Bream's is long) and by the number of the scales along the lateral line (the Bream has from 44 to 50, the Roach from 40 to 46).

For Roach hybrids see end of this chapter (page 176).

THE RUDD (*Scardinius erythrophthalmus*)

The Rudd is judged by many to be the handsomest freshwater fish of our isles. Its shape is intermediate between that of the Roach and the Bream, deeper than the former's and thicker than the latter's. It abounds in the Irish lakes, where it is called "roach," and is widespread in a haphazard way over England and Wales, where it is commonest in the Cam and Ouse districts and in the Broads. It has been introduced, probably during the eighteenth century, in many private ponds and canals, where it has prospered in the quiet waters it prefers.

It may be found in the slowest and weediest stretches of some rivers, where its habits are exactly those of the Roach; shoals composed of both species are frequently met. Ponds, fens and meres are the favourite home of the Rudd, and there you may observe it easily from a boat moored near a bank of reeds on a hot summer day. The Rudd cruise about among the weeds, picking insect larvae and shrimps off the stems and leaves of sedges or water-lilies, shaking them so that you may even think that a bird or a mouse is moving among them; or they will rise to the surface with a lively splash, noisier than those of Bream or Roach. You may catch a gleam of the gold and crimson of its livery when it takes a fly on the top of the water; if you want to make sure of seeing Rudd, throw a few dry crusts of bread here and there; they are sure to go nibbling at them like Bleak.

The Rudd has a deeper body than the Roach, its depth being from one-third to almost one-half the length of the fish. The back is dark blue or brown, the fins and the tail are deeply tinged with red; the lips are often outlined in crimson. The whole of the body is covered with a yellow shade that varies from light brass to deep gold. This golden colour is very variable according to place (I know two ponds in Bedfordshire about a mile from each other; in one the Rudd are as golden as Goldfish, in the other they are of a pale yellow colour), and according to season and individual. After death it disappears more or less completely, leaving the angler a difficult problem in distinguishing Roach from Rudd, not to mention hybrids such as Roach × Rudd, Roach × Bream and Rudd × Bream.

The *scales are large*, so that Dante mentions them for one of his wonderful comparisons; *they number from 39 to 44* (less than Roach or Bream) along the lateral line. The *dorsal fin* has a practically

straight margin, and is placed *well after* the beginning of the ventral
fins and consequently where the back is sloping towards the tail.
The *mouth* is rather oblique and the *lower lip* sticks out.   The
colour of the eye, that has given this species the local name of
"Red-eye," as well as its unspellable second scientific name, is too
much a question of personal opinion to be of any great use in
identifying a dead specimen.

The spawning habits of the Rudd are like those of the Roach,
and the development of the egg and fry is the same.   The
minimum legal size is also the same for the two fish.   Length for
length, the Rudd is the heavier fish, on account of its greater

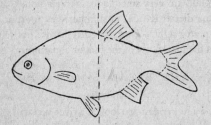

Fig. 10—Shape and position of fins in Rudd

depth of body.   The largest British Rudd caught by anglers is
one of 4½ lb. from a pond near Thetford, Norfolk, captured in
1933.   Rudd over 3 lb. are more common than Roach of the
same weight, but specimens over 2 lb. are nowadays rather uncommon.

Rudd can be fished for as Roach, remembering that it feeds
higher up in the water.   Fly-fishing is both enjoyable and profitable, especially on warm summer days.   In the cold months,
when Roach are still feeding merrily, Rudd are seldom caught.
A boat is often necessary to reach the best spots.

The flesh of the Rudd is of poor quality and comparable to
that of the Bream.

IDENTIFICATION.   Rudd are easily mistaken for *Roach*, less
easily for *Silver Bream* or *Goldfish*.   If the fish has a golden colour

and red fins, it is a Rudd; if it is golden with pale fins and a *long dorsal fin*, it is a Goldfish.   To distinguish it from Roach, remember that the Rudd's mouth has a projecting *lower* lip; the *dorsal fin* begins *behind* the ventral fins and ends almost above the vent. To distinguish at once from Silver Bream, remember that the *anal fin* of the Roach and Rudd is *short* (the branched rays are not more than 13), while in the Silver Bream it is long (not less than 19 rays).   If your specimen has characteristics between those of the Roach and those of the Rudd (accompanied usually by a pale brassy colour), it is probably a Roach × Rudd hybrid, but only a fish specialist will be able to tell.

Small Rudd are very suitable for garden ponds, and prosper on the same diet as Roach; in summer they sport at the surface and are a pretty sight.   They are fairly hardy, but require more room than the glass bowl of the indoor aquarium.

THE BLEAK (*Alburnus lucidus*)
Plate 11

When on a sunny day you look at a river you will see small fish darting here and there on the surface, splashing merrily, jumping over leaves and sticks floating on the stream, and rising at flies or thistledown.   Their sides are so bright and silvery that they flash in the sun, and you would think that Bleak was not a good choice of name.   There is nothing bleak about this pretty and jolly fish, enjoying life so fully and merrily, forgetting the gulls sweeping down from the sky, or the Pike and Trout darting from the weeds or the shadow of a bush.   If you are pedantically inclined, you may be interested to know that Bleak is etymologically connected with *bleach* and not *bleak*.   And if there are any women readers of this book, perhaps they may be interested to know that those merry Bleak have been killed by the million in some countries so that out of the scales of six or seven thousand of them might be extracted a pound of a shining substance that, mixed with wax, is used to fill artificial pearls.

The Bleak is distributed widely but irregularly in England and

Wales, and is not found in rivers opening in the Channel, in the Lake District, or in Ireland or Scotland.

Solemn and earnest anglers hate the frolicsome Bleak, that take the bait meant for Roach or better fish; haven't I read that those merry little creatures are pests that ought to be destroyed? Still, it is very easy to get rid of them from your "swim": cast a crust upon the waters, and the Bleak will follow it down the stream, nibbling at it in little shoals and occasionally lifting it out of the water. Truly the *manière forte* is fashionable to-day, even if in the long run it is far from being as effective as simple methods based on knowledge of Nature, including human nature.

Walton calls the Bleak *freshwater-sprat*, and the definition is apt; the green back, the silvery sides, the narrow long body resemble those of the Sprat. It has an *oblique mouth* and a projecting lower jaw. The dorsal fin is short, with 7 to 9 branched rays, while the anal is longer than in any of the Carp fishes that we have yet considered, having no less than 15 *rays and no more than* 20. The scales in *the lateral line are from* 46 *to* 54. The *fins are greenish or whitish*.

Bleak can be *easily distinguished* from small Chub, Dace or Roach by the *long anal fin*, which in the other three species is short, having from 10 to 13 rays; the oblique mouth also helps in identifying the Bleak.

This fish is angled mostly as bait for bigger game; it is seldom longer than 6 in., and specimens over 8 in. are rare. The largest on record weighed 5¼ oz. and was caught in the Trent in 1890.

The Bleak can be easily caught in summer by fishing rather high on the water, using very small hooks baited with bread, maggots or flies. It may also be angled by fly-fishing; there is no need to indulge in metaphysical problems of shades and shapes, because any small dark fly, wet or dry, will do, provided one strikes very quickly.

Bleak spawn in late spring, gathering on shallow water, as most other members of the family, showing the same excitement or possibly more. The eggs are slightly sticky. It would seem that the usual heedlessness that marks the actions of the Bleak is shown even in spawning, and the result is a large and varied collection of hybrids, some of which are described at the end of this chapter.

Bleak make fairly good eating, especially fried, although I find some difficulty in accepting Walton's statement that "bleaks be most excellent meat." They are rather delicate and die soon if roughly handled. They are unsuited to aquaria or very small ponds, but may thrive in larger ponds, especially if there is a gentle flow of water.

THE COMMON BREAM (*Abramis brama*)
(*Bronze Bream, Carp Bream*)

There is a certain kind of important person who invariably reminds me of Bream. I mean that special brand of successful financier, head of a great concern, influential politician, club-man, big Civil Servant, country magistrate and the like, so obviously marked in block letters "IMPORTANT."

The Bream, seen on its side, is a very imposing and portly fish, but seen from above is very narrow and flat, so as to justify the nickname of "bellows." For such an extensive body, it has a very small head and a small protruding eye. The general colour of the adult fish (by which time it is at least 10 in. long) is brown-ish with a bronze sheen that disappears after death; *the fins are browny black*. The young are silvery, with pale fins, and difficult to distinguish from those of the Silver Bream. The tail fin is deeply forked, and *the lower lobe is noticeably longer than the upper one*. The dorsal fin is *short*, usually with 3 single and 9 branched rays, very occasionally with 8 or 10. The anal fin is *long*, with *23 to 29 branched rays*. There are from *49 to 56 scales along the lateral line and 11 to 15 from the beginning of the dorsal fin to the lateral line*. The skin is rather slimy.

The Bronze Bream is very common in the eastern part of England and in Ireland; it is found also in Southern Scotland up to Loch Lomond, but not in Western Wales, Somerset, Cornwall,

Devon and Dorset. It prefers quiet water, such as lakes, canals and sluggish streams, provided they are deep and with muddy stretches. There it prowls about slowly in shoals, grubbing in the mud for anything eatable, such as worms, weeds, mud, larvae and shellfish. Its capacity for gorging is only too well known to anglers, who must throw an uncommon amount of ground bait into the "holes" of the river if they want to attract and keep Bream on the feed. After a couple of days of intensive ground baiting, it is possible to catch large numbers of Bream in a single night's fishing; though Bream bite even in daytime, the dark hours are best. The fish look heavier than they really are, and the average weight of those caught is two or three times that of the Roach from the same water. In the "good old days," anglers used to catch Bream by the stone or by the hundredweight, and we of the present day are now suffering for their greediness.

On sunny summer days one may see shoals of Bream forsaking their holes and coming near the top of the water, where they keep still, enjoying the warmth, sometimes rolling lazily on the surface before descending to the bottom to feed. They are also inclined to carry out large migrations from one spot to another, flitting mysteriously from an old haunt to a new residence, in shoals of many hundreds. These migrations cannot explain the strange disappearance of this fish from the lower reaches of the Thames, where it used to be very abundant. I cannot envisage Bream jumping like Salmon over Shepperton or Chertsey weirs.

The Bronze Bream grows into a big fish; one weighing 17 lb. was found once in the Trent, but the largest caught by fair angling weighed 12 lb. 15 oz. and was captured in Tring Reservoir in 1939. The minimum legal size is usually 12 in.; in the Broads the minimum is 8 in., a very low one.

Apart fom size and numbers, the Bream offers no particular interest. When hooked, it shows very little fight and allows itself to be hauled to the surface without any resistance except that offered by weight and width. The flesh is flabby and tasteless, with a strong muddy tang, and is comparable to that of Chub and Barbel.

The Bream spawns very late, in May and June, and during this period it forgets its usual stateliness and abandons itself to a noisy splashing advertisement of its loving disposition. The eggs are small, yellowish and very numerous, laid on weeds in the shallows near the banks; the oldest fish spawn first. The fry hatch out in 8 to 20 days, according to locality and temperature.

After spawning, the Bream goes back to its holes, instead of seeking fast-running water rich in oxygen as most other fish do.

The Bream forms hybrids with the Roach and with the Rudd, which may easily be mistaken for exceptionally large specimens of the two latter species. At the end of this chapter readers will find some data that may help them in avoiding this mistake.

Apart from its hybrids, the *young* of the Bronze Bream are *very easily mistaken* for *small* specimens of *Silver Bream*. If the fish is 10 or 12 in. long the difference is clear. For smaller sizes count *first* the branched rays in the anal fin: if they are more than 24, the fish is a Bronze Bream even if silvery. If the rays are between 19 and 22, the fish is probably a Silver Bream. You can make quite certain (when the fish has *from 22 to 24 rays*) by counting the scales along the lateral line (49 to 57 in the Bronze, 44 to 50 in the Silver) and between the start of the dorsal fin and the lateral line (11 to 15 in the Bronze, 8 to 11 in the Silver). The combination of two of these tests will certainly give you the identity of the specimen.

THE SILVER BREAM (*Blicca bjoernka*)
(*White Bream, Bream Flat*)
Plate 12

Many people in the Eastern Counties believe that this fish is simply the young of the Bronze Bream. As a matter of scientific fact, the two Breams are not even brothers, but merely cousins, with a different surname, justified by very good anatomical reasons. It is, however, quite true that small-sized specimens of the two Breams are often found together, and that they are hard to distinguish.

The Silver Bream is much less common than the Bronze, and its true home is in the rivers, canals and lakes of Eastern England, from the Thames basin to Yorkshire. It is found in ponds and lakes in other districts, where it has probably been introduced by people who thought they were stocking with Bronze Bream; as the young of both species are alike and go together, the mistake is very easy. In habits they are also very much alike.

The Silver Bream is even flatter than the Bronze, with a slightly larger eye and a slightly different snout. The back is greenish and the general appearance silvery. The fins are whitish, tinted with pink or orange in the adult fish; the dorsal has 3 simple and 8 branched rays (exceptionally 7 or 9); *the ventral is long, with 19 to 24 branched rays*; the tail fin is well forked, with the lower lobe slightly longer than the upper one. There are from 44 to 50 *scales along the lateral line*, and *from 8 to 11 in a transverse row* from the beginning of the dorsal fin to the lateral line.

This species does not reach the size of the Bronze Bream. Its average weight varies from 8 oz. to 1¼ lb.; the largest caught in Britain came out of a Gloucestershire lake in 1923, and weighed 4½ lb. Its sporting capacities are nil: it bites greedily and stupidly, and comes out of the water like a piece of weed. If you come across a shoal of this fish, you will get no chance of hooking anything better in that spot until the shoal has been caught. They are always lean, bony and slimy, and worthless as food. The curses that anglers heap on the unfortunate "tin plates" or "flatties," etc., are not without justification.

The spawning habits are the same as those of the Bronze kind, but a smaller number of eggs is laid.

HYBRIDS

CARP × CRUCIAN CARP. This hybrid has been found many times. It has either only one pair of small barbels or, if two pairs the front one is very small indeed. The dorsal fin is straight, the tail not very forked, the scales in the lateral line number from 33 to 38. All other characteristics intermediate between the two parents.

ROACH × RUDD. The similarity between the parents makes this hybrid rather difficult to recognize, and it may be commoner than it appears to be. The mouth is at the end of the snout, the scales in the lateral line number 42 or 43; the beginning of the dorsal fin is in a direct line above the middle of the ventral fins or over the tip of the little loose scale bordering these fins.

ROACH × BREAM. This is probably the commonest hybrid in British waters, and reputed exceptional specimens of Roach were often found to be this hybrid. It can be immediately distinguished from the Roach because the scales between the lateral line and the base of the ventral fins number 5 or 6, while in the Roach they vary between 3 and 4½ (in the Bream 6 or 7). The anal fin is longer and has from 15 to 19 branched rays (from 9 to 12 in the Roach, from 23 to 29 in the Bream). There are from 47 to 52 scales in the lateral line (from 40 to 46 in the Roach, from 49 to 57 in the Bream). All other characteristics are intermediate between the two parents.

RUDD × BREAM. This is rather similar to the Roach × Bream hybrid, differing in the same peculiarities that distinguish the Rudd from the Roach. The dorsal fin is farther back, the scales on the lateral line larger (and usually fewer), and the branched rays in the anal fin from 15 to 18. There is no room for error when this hybrid is found in the Irish lakes, which hold Rudd but no Roach. Mistakes are easier when the fish comes from East Anglian broads. It may be confused also with the Silver Bream (which has from 19 to 24 branched fin rays in its anal fin).

The hybrid between the *Rudd* and the *Silver Bream* has not been found yet in Britain; it may be distinguished from the preceding hybrid and from the Silver Bream by being not more than 10 in. in length, by having 40 to 46 scales on the lateral line, and only from 12 to 17 branched rays in the anal fin.

BLEAK × CHUB. Its peculiarities are: belly behind the ventral fins compressed to an edge—from 45 to 48 scales on the lateral line (Chub average 46, Bleak and Dace average 50)—forehead broader than in the Dace or Bleak—anal fin with 10 to 13 branched rays (Chub 8 to 9, Bleak 15 to 20). It may reach the length of a foot. It has been found in several localities. The hybrid *Bleak × Dace* would be rather similar, but smaller, with a narrower forehead and smaller mouth, and the dorsal and anal fins definitely concave, while the hybrid we have just described has them more or less straight.

BLEAK × ROACH. Rare; shares the qualities of both parents, and has also a belly compressed to a ridge; the branched rays in the anal fin are 13 in number (Roach 9 to 12, Bleak 15 to 20).

All the Bleak hybrids have a dorsal fin well behind the base of the ventral fins, about half-way between and above the ventral and anal fins. Other Bleak hybrids may be found, therefore anglers will do well to scrutinize fish that seem to have uncommon peculiarities.

24

THE LOACHES (*Cobitidae*)

Plate 13

THIS small group is related to the Carp family, and shares most of the characteristics of the fishes we have just described, such as the single dorsal fin, toothless mouth, teeth in the throat and soft fin rays.

There are two British species, very similar in appearance and habits. Both are *small*, have an *elongated body*, *very small scales*, rather difficult to see, *six barbels* round the mouth, small eyes, rather indistinct lateral line, *tail rounded with a single fluke*, body mottled, fins small and striped or dotted with dark marks. Both frequent the bottom of little clear streams and rills with a clean bed, but may be found in rivers, lakes and even ponds; they avoid the light, and usually lurk under a stone or a stick waiting for prey. Even when seen, they are difficult to grasp in the hand, because their long, slimy bodies slither easily out of an inexperienced hand. Walton praises their edible qualities, but it is not easy to collect these small fish in sufficient numbers to make a satisfactory dish. Their diet and their residence are so much like those of the Gudgeon that they are often caught when angling for this fish. They are mostly used as bait for Pike, Salmon and large Trout.

They are very hardy, and may even use gulps of air as an additional form of respiration. They are easily kept in aquaria and bowls (a young friend of mine treasured a Loach in the belief it was a special Catfish).

The STONE LOACH or COMMON LOACH (*Nemachilus* or *Cobitis barbatula*) fully justifies its names; it is nearly always under a stone, and it is certainly the commonest of the group, being found more or less everywhere in the British Isles except in the very North of Scotland. In colour it is grey-green or brownish, with irregular darker blotches and mottlings; the belly is white. It is usually about 3 to 4 in. in length, occasionally more. Its mouth has six barbels, *two of which*, at the corners of the jaws, *are longer than the others*.

The SPINY LOACH or GROUNDLING (*Cobitis taenia*) is much less common, and apparently is found only in some districts in England, such as the Trent basin, in the Ouse and Cam, in Wiltshire and Warwickshire. It is quite possible that its similarity to the other species and its small size have contributed to its remaining undetected in many of its haunts, and my readers would render useful service to naturalists by making known any discovery of this little fish in other districts. It is smaller than the Stone Loach, being usually not more then 3 in. long. The body is pale brown, with darker spots on the sides in a rather regular row. *All the six barbels are equally long*, and there is a *small double-pointed spine on the snout*, just below the eyes; this spine is *not fixed*, and when at rest it fits into a little groove below the eye. The body is more flattened than in the other species.

The Loaches are liable to be confused with the *Gudgeon* and the *Minnow*, both of which are blotched and spotted in the same colours. The Minnow, however, has *no barbels*, and the Gudgeon *only two*; both these fishes have *a forked tail*, unlike the Loaches.

Both Loaches spawn in late spring, but not much is known about their breeding habits. Here is another chance for the amateur to contribute to biological knowledge.

THE WELS (*Silurus glanis*)

The Wels or European Catfish is the biggest freshwater fish of Europe. During the last century attempts were made to introduce it into some British waters, especially in Essex. So far as I know, the fish has not prospered here, except for the famous specimens of Woburn Abbey, still surviving more than half a century after being imported. I believe it has disappeared from all the other localities where it was introduced. The Woburn fish do not seem to have become very large or to have multiplied.

The Wels is rounded, with a small single dorsal fin and a very long anal one, a broad head with a wide mouth and six long barbels. The short dorsal fin distinguishes it at first glance from the Burbot, the only British fish it resembles.

25

THE BURBOT (*Lota lota*—Cod family)
(*Barbolt, Eel-pout*)

THE young lady who was copying my manuscript of the General Section carefully changed Burbot to Turbot. When I timidly remarked that it really was Burbot, she stated firmly that *she* had *never* heard of such a fish, implying that both the Burbot and I were to blame. I, in my turn, shift the blame on the fish, which is both uncommon and of a retiring disposition. It is found only in the rivers of the East Coast from Suffolk to Durham, and is not particularly well known even to the local inhabitants, because it prefers rather deep water, where during the day it lies hidden among the weeds, or under stones, or in cracks or holes, rather like the Eel; and, again like the Eel, it goes about at night, voraciously eating worms, fish spawn, small fish or frogs.

The shape of the Burbot resembles that of its sea cousin, the Ling. It looks like a thick, portly Eel, with a mottled dark skin, the colour varying from yellowish to brown, the belly being pale yellow or white. The skin is thick and slimy, with numerous small scales. There are *two dorsal fins*, the first very short and the second very long; the tail fin is small and rounded; the small *ventral fins are placed on the throat* (typical of the Cod family), the anal fin is as long as the second dorsal; all the rays in the fins are soft. The mouth is large, with many bands of pointed teeth; the lower jaw bears *a central barbel*; two smaller barbels are found near the nostrils. The two dorsal fins, the barbels and the presence of two pairs of fins distinguish at first glance the Burbot from the Eel.

The largest Burbot recorded in the British Isles weighed 8 lb. and was caught in the Trent. The average weight is about 1½ lb., and a fish 2 ft. long and weighing 3 lb. is a good specimen. The Burbot is mostly caught on eel-lines baited with worms or small fish, or in eel-baskets, only occasionally falling to the Bream angler.

The Burbot spawns from January to March, assembling in shoals in shallow water; the numerous eggs are very small, yellowish and with an oil drop. They hatch out in about a month, and the heads of the young fry are bent queerly downwards. Growth is rapid, and in a year the young fish reach a length of about 4 in.; they are sexually mature in about three or four years.

The flesh of the Burbot has a high reputation on the Continent; it is firm and white, and may be fried, baked, steamed or stewed. When cleaning the fish, do not throw away the large oily liver: cut it into small bits, and cook it inside the fish; not only will the flavour be improved, but you will benefit from the oil which, like that of all the Cod family, is rich in vitamins.

26

THE PERCH FAMILY

In British waters there are two freshwater and one estuarine species of this family: the Perch, the Ruff and the Bass. The American Black Bass may be found in some waters.

The Perches belong to one of the most advanced groups of the Bony Fishes; one of their most obvious characteristics is the presence of two dorsal fins, the first composed of stiff spines, the second of soft rays (sometimes, as in the Ruff, the two fins are joined). There are also stiff, pungent spines at the beginning of the ventral and anal fins. The scales are tough, firmly fixed into the skin and rough to the touch, of the *ctenoid* type. The mouth is large, with numerous bristle-like teeth in the jaws. The gill-covers are spiky or toothed.

They can be easily distinguished because:

(*a*) The *Perch* has two separate dorsal fins, the first longer than the second; body deep, with five or more vertical dark bands; iris of eye golden.

(*b*) The *Ruff* is always small, has the spiny fin joined to the soft one, and the body is speckled; iris of eye mauve.

(*c*) The *Bass* is found in estuaries; body slim, grey and silver without bands or markings, dorsal fins approximately same size.

(*d*) The *Black Bass* has transversal stripes on its head; first dorsal fin smaller than second. Uncommon.

THE PERCH (*Perca fluviatilis*)

Plate 14

"The Pearch is a very good and a very bold biting fish. He is one of the fishes of prey that, like the pike and trout, carries his teeth in his mouth, which is very large. He has a hooked or hog back, which is armed with sharp and stiff bristles, and all his skin armed or covered over with thick dry hard scales, and hath, which few other fish have, two fins on his back." To complete

Walton's description, let us add that the colour is olive green on the back merging into yellow on the sides; the belly is white; the first dorsal fin has a black round spot at its end; the ventral and anal fins vary from orange to scarlet. There are usually five or six vertical dark bars (in young specimens there are often seven), which are occasionally divided in two on the back. The Perch is one of the handsomest of our freshwater fishes.

The Perch is very common all over the British Isles, except in Northern Scotland, in every kind of water, from the largest rivers and lakes to small gravel pits. In rivers it favours spots where the water flows slowly and where banks of weeds, snags, bridge piles, tangles of roots and the like give it suitable hiding-places from which to dart on shoals of fry or small fish. As a rule, Perch wander in small shoals composed of individuals of about the same size, keeping near the bottom. In lakes the size of the fish often increases with the depth of the bottom. On warm, calm summer days small shoals of Perch may occasionally be seen in mid-water and even near the surface, but this is not a common occurrence. In the cold months it seeks the deepest holes it can find, and feeds sparingly.

Small Perch are perhaps the easiest fish to hook. They are the classical victim of the "piece of string-bent-pin-worm" *ensemble* of the boy angler, but older Perch in public waters are far more wide awake, and their capture requires a good deal of skill, fine tackle and luck. The worms or small fish used for bait will be taken with typical boldness only if cunningly presented; a good Perch will fight to the last, doing its best to entangle the tackle in twigs and weeds and break it. There are records of 8 and 10 lb. Perch, but the largest British rod-caught fish (Norfolk, 1936), weighed 5 lb. ¾ oz. A 7-lb. Perch was caught in the Lee at Ballincollig (Cork) in 1899. Specimens over 2 lb. are to be considered good and over 3 lb. exceptional. The minimum legal size is normally 8 in. (9 in. in the Thames); these sizes mean weights of about 8 or 10 oz.; a fish 12 in. long weighs 1 lb., and one 15 in. about 1¾ lb.

In some ponds and lakes there are myriads of Perch of sardine size. In 1941 an experiment was carried out in Lake Windermere to trap these undersized fish and pack them in tins like sardines. I do not know whether the venture was successful, at least from a gastronomical point of view. Dr. Worthington, Secretary of the Fresh Water Biological Association, has stated that not only Char and Trout have benefited from the elimination of some three million stunted fish, but that the numerous Perch left in the lake have grown much larger than they used to be; an interesting example of that "ecological balance of life" that might find fruitful application in other spheres. In simple language, it means that overcrowding is bad for everybody, and that too little food for common small Perch is of no advantage to aristocratic Trout either.

Perch spawn in the spring, like other "coarse" fish. From March to May they take to weedy shallows, where they lay peculiar ribbons of jelly, in which the whitish eggs are embedded at regular intervals; these festoons of spawn resemble those laid by toads, and are considered a titbit, not only by all fish, but also by waterfowl, that destroy very large quantities of potential Perch. The fry hatch out in two or three weeks, according to the place and the temperature of the water. Development is rapid, and in a year the fish reach a length of 3 to 4 in.; they start spawning when three years old.

Perch are very hardy and tenacious of life, and small specimens live easily in aquaria, provided they are fed on animal food, such as worms, maggots or finely shredded raw heart, given a little at a time (bread is useless, and so are the so-called "ants' eggs"). They are colourful and interesting fish to observe, with a fairly wide range of changes and expressions, in which the large dorsal fin plays a great part, often to the accompaniment of alterations in colour. Unfortunately, according to my experience, they are liable to die suddenly without any visible cause.

The Perch is one of the very best fish from the culinary point of view, especially if coming from running water or gravelly

lakes. Its flesh is firm and white, without that muddy tang which
accompanies most freshwater fish. Fried, grilled or steamed, it is
always excellent. Recipes usually tell you to scale a Perch. I
wonder whether those who give this advice have ever tried to
scale a Perch. For my part I never bother, and prefer to remove
the skin after cooking. If you really want to scale the fish, put
on dungarees, place the Perch in the middle of a newspaper in the
yard, and *go to it*. At the end of the work (I am not misusing the
word), there will be scales in your hair, scales on your face and in
your eyes, scales decorating several square yards of the surrounding terrain, and, alas, scales still on the fish.

CAUTION. Perch have *very sharp spines* on the first dorsal fin
and at the beginning of the ventral and anal fins; there are also
very sharp edges and spikes *on the gill-covers*. When handling a
Perch be careful to avoid these parts (not easy with a vigorously
struggling fish), or your hands may be unpleasantly pricked.

THE RUFF OR POPE (*Acerina cernua*)

From Scotland and Ireland, as well as from some parts of England (that is, west of the Severn and Dee basins, and in the southern counties outside the Thames basin), the Ruff is absent.
Anglers elsewhere, in the eastern counties especially, may at times
wish that this small fish could also leave their waters and let them
angle peacefully for bigger game. You may hear anglers declare
that when there are Ruff in a spot they chase away all other fish
and that the fishing is ruined. This opinion is quite unfounded;
I have caught Perch, Gudgeon, Dace and Roach in spots crowded
with Ruff. I am ready, however, to admit that the quick-biting
Ruff will not give a chance to the slow Bream or Tench, and that
in such mixed company you will catch nothing but Ruff. What
is worse, many of these will probably gorge the hook, and you
may be obliged to kill and split open the unfortunate little glutton
before being able to resume your fishing. The Ruff competes
successfully with the small Perch or the Silver Bream, and

challenges the "bootlace" Eel, for the position of fish you don't *want* to catch.

No, the Ruff is not a favourite with anglers. It has the further disadvantages of being small, very slimy, and of having the pricking spikes of its family. All angling books either disregard it or damn it, with the exception of Walton, who proclaims it "an excellent fish, no fish that swims is of a pleasanter taste— taken to be better than the pearch."

The Ruff moves about in shoals where the water is slow and fairly deep, and keeps to the bottom, gulping down any small animal things passing within easy range, such as small crustacea, worms, larvae, fish spawn and fry. It is more thick-set than the Perch, and has the slightly flattened belly characteristic of bottom-living fish. It is seldom seen unless hooked when fishing for other fish, and in spite of its small size it fights with the vigour of a Perch twice its size; it has the curious habit of opening wide its gill-covers, possibly in order to bring into defence the sharp edges of those organs.

The general colour is olive grey fading to whitish on the belly, with numerous dark specks and spots. The spiny first dorsal fin is joined to the soft second dorsal; the fins on the belly are yellow; the eye is large and with a typical mauve iris. There are no official records of specimen Ruff, but Tate Regan states that it seldom exceeds a length of 7 or 8 in.

Spawning takes place in late spring, when numerous small eggs are laid in strings in the weedy shallows; they hatch out in 12 to 15 days.

The Ruff is hardy and lives easily in the aquarium, both indoors and outdoors. It takes the same food as the Perch. It is rather an uninteresting fish to keep, owing to its sluggishness and its love of keeping to the bottom, with which it merges so effectively as to be almost invisible.

In spite of its small size the Ruff is a dainty morsel, and may be fried with and as Gudgeon; remove the tough, rough skin before eating.

CAUTION. Handle Ruff with care, because the fins and gill-covers are supplied with needle-sharp points.

PERCH × RUFF HYBRIDS. The hybrid of these two species has not been found yet in British waters, though it has been obtained experimentally. It was first discovered in the Danube. The off-spring are intermediate between the two parents in character, in coloration and in number of scales and fins. As a rule, the peculiarities of the mother are the most prominent, and therefore the offspring of male Ruff and female Perch will show the bars of the mother with the speckles of the father, while that of a male Perch and female Ruff will be very similar to a normal Ruff.

THE BASS (Morone labrax)

In the estuaries where there are no Salmon, anglers are very fond of calling this fish "Salmon Bass," an innocent form of snobbery based upon the outward similarity between the two species. In spite of the flattering name, the Bass is not even remotely connected with the Salmon family, being a Sea Perch (Serranid), with the spiny first dorsal fin and spiky gill-covers of all Perches.

The Bass is common along the southern and western coasts of the British Isles, especially in the warmer months. It keeps near the shore, and has a preference for estuaries, journeying up the rivers for many miles. It spawns in these months, either in salt or in fresh water; the eggs sink to the bottom in fresh water, but in the sea they float.

The body of the Bass is silvery, with a silvery blue back and a dark spot on the gill-cover. Young specimens ("school Bass") have numerous dark specks on their sides that may tempt some anglers into visions of Sea Trout or grilse. The absence of the "adipose" finlet and the presence of two distinct dorsal fins (the first spiky) ought to make such a mistake easily avoidable.

The Bass is a very voracious, powerful, capricious and cunning fish, and its capture is unpredictable, as any Bass specialist will acknowledge. Its food consists of small fish, crustaceans (prawns and soft crabs being favourites), worms and (for old and big fish) the foulest garbage found in harbours. The biggest specimen (16 lb.) angled in the British Isles fell in 1909 to the fly of a Trout angler fishing in the Waterville estuary in Ireland. The biggest sea specimen (16½ lb.) was caught in the Menai Strait. A fish half these weights will supply any angler with joy and stories for many years.

A smallish Bass, not over 3 or 4 lb., is one of the best fish for the table; it may be cooked and served as a Trout. Bigger specimens tend to be coarse, unless they have been in fresh water for some time. The French and the Italians grow lyrical when discussing the culinary merits of the Bass, contrary to the British, who know it almost exclusively as a very game fish, to be angled only for the sport of catching it.

THE BLACK BASSES (*Micropterus*)

Attempts have been made in some English rivers (especially in Cornwall and Devon) to acclimatize a well-known sporting fish of North American lakes and rivers, the Black Bass (family Centrarchidae). The results have not been too successful, and the fish are uncommon, except occasionally in some private waters.

There are two species, the Small-mouthed and the Large-mouthed Black Bass, very similar to each other in general appearance. Both have two dorsal fins, the first of which is spiny and shorter and lower than the second. The snout is sharper than in the Perch, the eye larger. The body is covered with irregular vertical bands of rows of dark dashes. The head bears on each side four or five transversal dark stripes; this coloration is more marked in the young.

The *Small-mouth* (*Micropterus Dolomieu*) reaches in America the weight of about 4 lb. The upper jaw ends just below the eye —there are more than 72 scales along the lateral line, and 11 between the first dorsal fin and the lateral line.

The *Large-mouth* (*Micropterus salmoides*) may reach a weight of

8 lb. The upper jaw extends far beyond the eye—there are from 65 to 70 scales along the lateral line and 7 to 8 between the first dorsal and the lateral line.

THE PIKE-PERCH

The PIKE-PERCH (*Lucioperca sandra*) has been introduced in some private waters. It is a Continental species, much esteemed for its sporting and culinary qualities. It is marked like a Perch and shaped like a Pike, with the two typical dorsal fins of the Perch group. The first dorsal has no black spot. The colour is dark grey on the back, silvery on the belly; the teeth are large.

27

THE GREY MULLETS (*Mugilidae*)

THERE are three British species of Grey Mullets, all very alike in appearance and habits. They are sea fish, but they keep near the shore, and are fond of harbours and estuaries, where they spawn in the spring. Like the Bass, they enter rivers at high tide, sometimes for many miles, and Walton mentions "an Arundel Mullet" as one of the special boasts of Sussex.

All our Grey Mullets have a broad head rather like a Chub's and a broad back of a metallic blue; the sides are silvery with numerous thin blue-grey longitudinal stripes; the belly is white. They have *two short dorsal fins*, the first with four spines, the second with a spine and eight or nine soft rays. The mouth is small and fringed with feeble bristle-like teeth, suitable for a soft diet of mud, fine seaweeds, small creatures and decomposing animal or vegetable stuff. *The head is scaly. There is no lateral line.*

The THICK-LIPPED GREY MULLET (*Mugil chelo*) is probably the commonest. It has a *thick upper lip with tiny warty protuberances*, and its *pectoral fin is at least three-fourths of the length of the head.*

The THIN-LIPPED GREY MULLET (*Mugil capito*) has a *thin, smooth upper lip*; its pectoral fin is *less* than three-fourths of the length of the head; above the upper corner of the pectoral fin is a rather pointed *long scale* half-detached from the body, resembling a tiny fin.

The GOLDEN GREY MULLET (*Mugil auratus*) is very rare. It is recognizable by two golden spots on the head, one on the gill-cover and the other behind the eye.

All Grey Mullets have a well-deserved reputation for being exceedingly difficult to angle. In southern and western harbours it is possible in summer to see shoals of Grey Mullets sporting in the water without paying the smallest attention to the anglers' hooks, baited with a wondrous selection of baits. The Mullets have earned the name of Carp of the sea; the capture of these shy and cunning fish is not easy by any method, netting not excepted.

A 16¾-lb. Grey Mullet was netted in the Pagham lagoon (Sussex), but such a specimen is a rarity, and a fish over 3 lb. is a fine catch for any angler.

Fried, grilled, stewed or steamed, Grey Mullets are delicious, and enjoy a high reputation in the Mediterranean.

28

THE BULLHEAD OR MILLER'S THUMB
(*Cottus gobio*—Bullhead family)
Plate 15

THIS oddly named and oddly shaped little fish has such retiring habits and protective coloration that it is far less known than one would expect from its wide distribution. It is to be found in most waters in England and Wales; I have been assured that it exists in some of the southernmost streams of Scotland. It is absent from Ireland, according to Tate Regan, but the official Irish Anglers' Guide does not mention the Bullhead among the English fish not found in Ireland.

In these days of gigantic mills to say that something looks like a miller's thumb would not help anybody; millers are important gentlemen in City offices, and their fingers are nicely shaped and nicely cared for. Some young friends of mine, looking down at a Bullhead in a little stream, have compared it to a mandoline, or a big tadpole, or a prehistoric man's club. This small fish, seen from above, shows *a large flattened head* made more conspicuous by wide gill-covers, armed with a sharp curved spine, and *large pectoral fins* behind which the body tapers quickly away to the tail. It has *two dorsal fins* close together, the *first short* and with slightly stiffer spinous rays than the second. The anal fin is rather long and the tail fin is rounded. The skin is *scaleless*, brownish on the back and fading to yellowish white on the belly, with numerous blotches of brownish black; the colour changes very quickly. The fins are striped with dark bands. The size reached is about 3 or 4 in., very exceptionally 6 in. The mouth is large, well supplied with minute teeth, and the Bullhead uses it with great initiative in swallowing any creature that might get into it, from insect larvae and worms to fish not much smaller than the hunter itself. As Walton says, "he never refuses to bite," and if a hook baited with worm or maggot passes near his mouth it will certainly be taken. When unhooking it, do not forget the sharp spines on the gill-covers, or you may be reminded of them pretty quickly.

The Bullhead prefers clean water, especially if there are pebbles at hand under which it can take cover, or gravel in the midst of which the mottled body of the fish becomes invisible. It may be found in the smallest mountain streams, as well as in lakes and large rivers. You may observe it sometimes resting immovable on the bottom, and making sudden rapid dashes here and there to gulp food. Its immobility may tempt you to try to catch it in your hand: you will discover, if you are lucky, that the Bullhead is a quicker mover than you thought; if you are nimble, and unlucky, you will seize the fish—and its spines.

The Bullhead is normally a solitary fish; in the spawning season (early spring) the fish pair off and deposit their eggs in a rough little redd in the gravel, under the shelter of a stone. The eggs are larger than those of the members of the Carp family, and are laid in a pinkish cluster of a few hundred, seldom more than a thousand. The male fish guards the eggs and the young fry for about four weeks.

What little meat there is on the fish is sweet-tasting, and Walton praises it highly. It is very hardy and tenacious of life, and can be kept easily in an aquarium, feeding it as Perch or Ruff, but taking care not to put into its company any other small fish. Its odd shape, rapid changes of colour, and sudden dashes make it a rather interesting inhabitant of indoor aquaria, provided they are not too small and have a layer of gravel at the bottom.

29

THE STICKLEBACKS (*Gasterosteidae*)
(Tiddler, Tittlebat, Prickleback, Stickling, Jack-sharp, Bar-stickle, etc.)

Plate 16

IF I were asked which British freshwater fish I consider the most ferocious, I would not answer Trout, Eel or even Pike: I would without hesitation award this undesirable pre-eminence to the Stickleback, that fierce attacker of other creatures even bigger than itself, that voracious devourer of small fry. If the innumerable Sticklebacks of our shores and rivers were as large as Pike, they would make our waters more dangerous, even to man, than if they were inhabited by alligators. Dip your walking-stick in the midst of a shoal of Tiddlers, and they will attack it with such vigour that you will feel the impact of their tiny bodies against the wood. You may keep a few Sticklebacks in an aquarium, but they will kill and tear to pieces any small Goldfish or other defenceless small fish; only Gudgeon and Loaches, that hug the bottom of the tank, may escape the murderous spines of the little terrorists.

There are two species living in our ponds and streams, the Three-spined and the Ten-spined. Both, especially the former, are also found in brackish and salt water.

The THREE-SPINED STICKLEBACK (*Gasterosteus aculeatus*), together with tadpoles and young fry, are the children's first captures in the stream or pond near home. Heaven knows how many Salmon, Shark and Tunny anglers began with a tiddler, caught with a worm tied to a piece of string. It is a small species, usually about 2 in. in length or less, and never more than four. It bears *two strong spines on its back*, followed by a third and smaller one that precedes a soft dorsal fin. The ventral fins are reduced to a strong spine and a ray; this soft ray can be worked by the fish as a " catch " on the joint of the spine, which sticks out firmly as a powerful offensive weapon, much used by its owner in its attacks and fights. The anal fin is under the soft dorsal, about the same length, and also preceded by a short spine. The mouth is small, oblique, with rows of sharp teeth. The body is more or less covered with narrow but rather deep little bony shields or *scutes*, with a ridge in the middle. These scutes take the place of scales, and are not uniformly distributed on every fish. There are three principal varieties, which in the old days were granted the high rank of species. In one, the "rough-tailed" (G. *trachurus*), the shields are arranged in a regular and complete series from the head to the tail. This variety is commonest in the sea and in estuaries, especially in the northern parts of our islands. Another form, the "half-armed" (G. *semiarmatus*), has a few scutes behind the head and a few more on the sides of the tail, the space between being bare; it is found mostly in estuaries and brackish water. The third variety, the "smooth-tailed" (G. *gymnurus*), is the usual one in inland waters, and bears only a few shields after the gill-covers, the rest of the body being naked. The three forms may be found in the same shoal, with intermediate varieties bearing a different number of shields; occasionally a specimen may be rough-tailed on one side and half-armed on the other. Sticklebacks with four dorsal spines are not uncommon, but those with only two are very rare. The farther north one goes, the more marine is this fish and its spines and scutes are stronger; travelling southwards it is found more and more frequently in inland waters, so that in the Mediterranean it is a freshwater species; a behaviour parallel to that of the Trout.

The Stickleback lives in small shoals, preferring ditches, little streams and the shallows of rivers and ponds, hunting with great pertinacity any and every animal form that may be devoured—insects, worms, fish spawn and baby fry being the favourite diet. It has a green back and silvery sides, shot with pale blue and pink. In the spawning season, which varies from year to year and from place to place, the male fish becomes brightly coloured: its sides are striped with dark bands, and its belly is vivid red; the female is more simply dressed, her belly becoming yellow. The Stickle-backs build nests for their offspring, an uncommon custom among fishes. We have already described (page 37) the nest-building, courtship and other spawning habits of this fish.

In some countries, where Sticklebacks are very abundant, they are caught in fine nets, oil is extracted from them and the residue is used as a fertilizer. In Britain, apart from supplying children with easy captures and anglers with live-bait, it enters in a small proportion into the so-called "Whitebait," which consists mostly of Herring and Sprat fry. Its economic value does not com-pensate, even in the slightest, for its rapacious destruction of fish eggs and fry, from Trout to Roach.

The TEN-SPINED STICKLEBACK (*Gasterosteus* or *Pygosteus pungitius*) is an even smaller species, seldom reaching 3 in. in length. It has from eight to eleven short spines on the back, bent alternately to the right and to the left, rather like the teeth of a saw. It is not so common or so widespread as its three-spined cousin, and is not found in Scotland north of Loch Lomond. It is principally a freshwater fish, but may be found in brackish water. A variety found in some parts of Ireland has no ventral fin or spine. In colour it is greenish olive with numerous dark dots, becoming blue-brown in the spawning season. For the rest this fish resembles the Three-spined in appearance and habits. The nest is not built on the bottom, as in the other species, but is hung on to weeds, a little above the bottom, close to the bank.

We have been told that the "Observations on the Theory of Tittlebats," by Samuel Pickwick, G.C.M.P.C., were received with "feelings of unmingled satisfaction and unqualified approval" by his fellow club members. Anyone who has paid a little attention to the much-ridiculed Stickleback will be more in-clined to agree with those earnest seekers after knowledge, the members of the Pickwick Club, than with their famous chronicler.

30

THE FLOUNDER (*Pleuronectes flesus*—Plaice family)
(Fluke, Butt)

THE Flatfish Order (*Heterosomata*) is a large one, almost exclusively marine and of great economic importance. The true Flatfishes, such as the Plaice, the Halibut or the Turbot, are flattened on their sides, and swim on one of them. The Rays and Skates are flattened back to belly, with the mouth on the underside of the head. The Flatfish's mouth is at the end of the snout; both eyes are on one side of the body, and only this side is coloured, the blind one being white or light-coloured. Most of the British species have eyes on their right side (Plaice, Dab, Halibut, Sole, etc.), and only a few on the left (Turbot, Brill, Topknots).

Of the many species found in our seas only one, the Flounder, enters fresh water, and actually prefers estuaries and lagoons to the open sea. About 1836, according to Yarrell, this fish was common in the Thames as far upstream as Sudbury, but nowadays it is only to be found in the lower reaches of the estuary, and it is the same with other poisoned rivers. That it can live in upper waters is proved by the fact that (before weirs were built near Gloucester) Flounders were common near Shrewsbury and were recorded even in Montgomeryshire.

When found in completely fresh water this fish cannot be mistaken for any other, but in tidal stretches of estuaries it may easily be confused with Dab and Plaice. However, if you rub the coloured side of a Dab you will immediately identify it by its rough surface; the lateral line of the Dab curves above the pectoral fin to make a half-circle, while in the Flounder and the Plaice the line is almost straight. The Plaice has an irregular bony ridge on the head, and large and conspicuous orange spots on its coloured side, while the Flounder has rows of small knobs along the lateral line and the long fins.

As we saw in the General Section, the Flounder varies its colour to a very great degree. In a muddy estuary such as the Thames its coloured side will be black, while on a clean sandy shore it will be greyish; its skin may also be mottled, marbled or spotted, according to the bottom on which the fish lives. It often has orange spots, though they are never so large as those of the Plaice. The blind side of the fish is usually dead white, but specimens coloured on both sides are not uncommon, and in some places a large percentage of Flounders are left-sided (that is, they have their eyes on the left side of the body, instead of the right, as is usual). This fish often has small tumours on its skin, caused by a parasite, and another parasite is sometimes found on its pectoral fins.

The Flounder may reach a length of 18 in. ; the largest specimen angled in Britain was captured in 1934 (Tees Mouth) and weighed 4 lb. 1 oz., but fish even half that weight are exceptional. The average caught is about the size of a hand or less. A great many Flounders are caught in stake-nets, and immense quantities of immature fish are destroyed by shrimp trawls, together with the young of other Flatfish.

The Flounder is rather a sluggish fish and spends a good deal of its time half buried in estuary mud. When the tide rises, the Flounders follow it, swimming short distances near the bottom, on which they rest at intervals. Their food consists of small shellfish, worms and shrimps. The Flounder may be angled. using worms or shrimps as bait, and in spite of its small size it gives a good account of itself on light tackle. Where the water is shallow and clear, it is possible to spear the fish with a fork (a fishing, not a table, fork). As a rule, the flesh is not particularly good, although in some favourable localities it is of fair quality. The best method of cooking a Flounder is that of the fried-fish shop, where many "plaice" are Dabs and Flounders.

The Flounder spawns from February to May, in deeper water than the fish normally inhabits. The eggs are small and very numerous, the average number being about a million. The fry hatch out after a period of incubation lasting from 6 to 12 days, according to the temperature. Like other Flatfish, the baby Flounder starts life as a normal "straight" fish, and begins swimming on one side only about a month later.

31

BOOKS TO READ

I MAY have succeeded in awakening in you a certain interest in fishes. You might want to know more about them; you may want to study them, or catch them, or maybe only cook them better.

If you want to read more on Fishes, borrow at your library a few books by E. G. Boulenger, the former Director of the Zoo's Aquarium. His books are written in a very pleasant and accessible way, and luckily are to be found in practically every library. If you would like to know more about the life of fishes in general, you could hardly do better than read J. R. Norman's *A History of Fishes*; it is packed full of an incredible amount of interesting information; the only fault of this book, but a very bad one, is that it is out of print. For the detailed study of British freshwater fishes there is nothing better than C. Tate Regan's book of the same name. If you want to know also about sea species, I strongly advise you to read *The Fishes of the British Isles*, by J. Travis Jenkins. Seashore life is most interestingly described (and beautifully photographed) by D. P. Wilson in his *Life of the Shore and of the Shallow Sea*.

I have already given you advice about aquaria. If you want to set out as a Brother of the Angle you have a wealth of books to help you, from Izaak Walton's *Compleat Angler* to the latest angling manual. Among the best known and most useful I should put the works of "John Bickerdyke," Francis, Martin, Sheringham, Marston, Cooper, Bazley, Turing, Holcombe and many others, among which I particularly recommend Marshall Hardy.

Excellent recipes for cooking fish are found in two books by the well-known culinary expert Ambrose Heath.

The books I have named contain further lists of books you may consult with profit; with knowledge, as with many other things,

it is just a question of starting. As that old scoundrel (I mean
realistic politician) Talleyrand said, "Pour arriver, on arrive
toujours—pourvu qu'on part." You may arrive anywhere—
provided you start.

32

LIST OR GLOSSARY OF SPECIAL TERMS

abdominal, of the pelvic fins: on the belly.

adipose fin: small fatty fin before the tail.

anadromous: (a fish) leaving the sea to spawn in rivers.

anal fin: fin after the vent.

barbel: skin filament or wattle hanging from mouth.

cartilage: gristle.

caudal fin: tail fin.

coloration: combination of colour with pattern in animals.

crustacean: aquatic animal with more than six jointed legs, and a hard outer shell-skin (shrimp, crab, water fleas, etc.).

ctenoid (scale): rough, with comb-like edge (Perch).

cycloid (scale): round, smooth-edged (Carp, Herring).

demersal (fish egg): lying on the bottom.

dorsal fin(s): fin or fins on the back.

ecology: study of plants and animals in connection with their surroundings.

ichthyology: study of fishes, fishlore.

insect: small animal in three sections, with six jointed legs, breathing air (flies, butterflies, beetles, fleas, bugs, etc.).

jugular (of the pelvic fins): on the throat.

larva: young animal structurally different from adult.

lateral line: a line going usually from the gills to the tail on the side of the body of most fishes.

mollusc: animal with soft body, that may be enclosed by a single shell (snail), two (mussel), or with an internal support (squid, cuttlefish).

nekton: swimming forms of life.

pectoral fins: first pair of fins, usually behind gills.

pelagic: floating egg of fish.

pelvic fins: also called ventral—second pair of fins, usually after the pectorals.

plankton: floating forms of life, usually small.

pollution: poisoning of water by filth, sewage and industrial refuse.

ray: soft-branched bone supporting fin.

redd: spawning bed of salmon.

spine: stiff single bone supporting fin (occasionally by itself).

thoracic (of the pelvic fins): on the chest.

ventral fins: see "pelvic."

vertebra: a section of the backbone.